FIRST WOMAN EDITOR

Sarah J. Hale

Born: October 24, 1788
Died: April 30, 1879

Books by Olive Burt

JEDEDIAH SMITH
Fur Trapper of the Old West

OURAY THE ARROW

JOHN CHARLES FREMONT
Trail Marker of the Old West

BRIGHAM YOUNG

JIM BECKWOURTH
Crow Chief

FIRST WOMAN EDITOR
Sarah J. Hale

FIRST WOMAN
EDITOR

Sarah J. Hale

by

Olive Burt

Julian Messner, Inc.
New York

Published by Julian Messner, Inc.
8 West 40 Street, New York 18

Published simultaneously in Canada
by The Copp Clark Publishing Co. Limited

Second Printing, 1960

Printed in the United States of America

Library of Congress Catalog Card No. 60-7818

To my "Granddaughters"
Rebecca, Louise, Marian and Jane
and to their mother,
sharer of hilarious recollections of our
newspaper days

Contents

Contents

FIRST WOMAN EDITOR

Sarah J. Hale

1

AN INTERRUPTED TEST

SARAH BUELL, RIDING HER SMALL GRAY MARE DOWN THE steep mountain road, was unconscious of the frown that wrinkled her broad forehead. But she was not unaware of the fact that she was worried. The April breeze lifted the hem of her long gray homespun dress, neatly arranged to cover her feet as she sat sidewise on the saddleless animal. She hoped the wind would not ruffle her curls, carefully tucked under a net. For today, Sarah felt, she must look as prim and staid as it was possible for a pretty, fun-loving eighteen-year-old girl to look.

Today was the annual examination day in the little Newport township school in western New Hampshire, where Sarah had been teaching all winter. Selectman Giddings with two townsmen of his choice would visit the school to judge the effectiveness of her teaching methods. And upon their judgment depended her chance of having the school again next winter.

"I'm not afraid of what the children will do," Sarah said aloud to her horse, Graybird. "They know their lessons well. But it's myself that may cook my goose, as Lottie would say." She reached down a small, carefully cared-for hand to pat

11

the mare's neck. "Do you think I'll make a good impression, Graybird?" she asked softly. "You know how old Silas Giddings fought against my having the position last fall. He said women were not fit to be teachers, and that I was too young anyway. Too young to teach! He wouldn't think I was too young to marry and bear children, but I am too young to teach them in school! And I had turned eighteen!" She smiled, remembering the family party given for that important birthday on October 24, 1806, with the whole family at home and Lottie outdoing herself with special dishes. Her two brothers, Charles and Horatio, had teased her about being grown up at last, while sixteen-year-old Martha Maria had watched with envious but affectionate eyes, longing for her own adulthood.

Sarah lifted her face and drew in a deep breath. The trees and shrubs and grass, dampened by the heavy dew, gave off a rich, earthy aroma that she loved. Violets poked their purple heads up from their glossy leaves and wake-robins dotted the path. Sugar River, tumbling along nearby, sang a merry tune. Breathing deeply of the perfumed air, Sarah felt her worries melt away in the sheer enjoyment of the bright spring morning.

She had ridden that mountain road when it had not been so pleasant. During the deep snows and bitter winds of the past winter, and during the heavy rains of March, she had traveled these two miles between her home on East Mountain and the school. She had seldom let the weather dictate her actions, and only the very worst storms had been able to keep her at home. She knew then that the children would not venture forth to school and the trip would be useless.

On this morning the ride from her father's farmstead to the little brown schoolhouse was sheer joy, and Sarah's confidence was still firm as she dismounted in the schoolyard. She tethered Graybird where the grass was thick and removed the bridle so that the mare could munch on the succulent green while her mistress was busy. Then she hurried into the schoolroom, glad that she was ahead of her pupils. It gave her time to whisk a dustcloth over desks and benches, to see that the pine table which served her for a desk was in apple-pie order. She had just finished these chores and was stooping to look at herself in the tin reflector behind the seldom-used candle sconce when the door was flung open and the first children came bouncing in.

Sarah turned and greeted them, noting with satisfaction that Amasa Leavitt had donned a clean shirt. She gave him a smile and the boy beamed at her.

"Anythin' I kin do to help, Miss Sary?" he asked hopefully.

"You may check the slates, Amasa. See that each desk has one and that it is clean."

"Can I help him?" piped up little Mary Tucker.

"I wish you would, Mary," Sarah said.

Other children were arriving, and Sarah, standing straight and prim beside her desk, greeted each with a smile and a special word. How wonderful they were! She had told them how important today was; she had taken them into her confidence, placing upon them part of the responsibility for the day's success.

"We must make a good showing when the examiners come on Friday. Everything depends on it, for if we don't pass the tests with flying colors—well, that will mean that I cannot be your teacher next year—"

"Oh! Oh no!"

Sarah felt a warm flush rise to her cheeks at the exclamation.

Then Cora Whiting had stood up with determination.

"Don't you worry one bit, Miss Sarah, we'll do you proud. We've learned a lot this winter, haven't we?" She turned to her classmates and they nodded vigorously,

Sarah smiled suddenly. "I'm sure you will. I'm not worried about *you*. I just wanted you to know that it is important to *me*—for I want to be with you again next year."

And here they were, their faces scrubbed till they glistened; their patched and faded clothing as clean as lye and homemade soap could get them. Their hair was brushed and pulled back from their eager faces, their eyes were shining. Sarah felt a lump rise in her throat. Old Mr. Giddings could not take this school away from her! No matter what he thought about girls and women, he could not deny that these children were not only learning, they were eager to learn. And some of them—her eyes rested on Cora—had so much promise! She could not turn them over to the dull, unimaginative methods of the usual schoolmaster or schoolmarm.

Just as she reached that conclusion she heard, through the open door, the wheezy voice of the selectman, instructing his companions as they neared the building.

"Mebbe she is purty—too purty for a schoolteacher! But don't let that tint yore jedgment, Jed Clough! If she ain't taught them childern their readin', an' writin', and figures, out she goes. I don't have no child in her school, but I've heard things——"

"Let's wait, Silas," came a quiet voice, which Sarah recognized as that of Lewis Richards, whose daughter Myra was one of her brightest pupils.

Sarah felt relieved at the sound of those other voices. With Lew Richards and Jed Clough as members of the examining committee, she should not fare too badly. She cast a swift glance at her pupils. Their eyes answered with a bright promise to do their best, and she stepped to the door to welcome the men.

"Good morning, Mr. Giddings," she said pleasantly, extending her hand to the dour farmer who had been her most uncompromising critic. Inwardly, she felt a slight twinge of conscience at being so pleasant to him, but she knew that she must be tactful.

The old man shook her hand, peering past her into the room, his eyes sharp to catch something to censure. The children rose, each one standing stiffly beside the long bench. As the old man came inside the girls curtsied, the boys bent their heads, and all said clearly, "Good morning, sir!"

The selectman nodded curtly in answer to the greeting. Sarah spoke to the other men and asked them all to take seats on the small raised platform at the front of the room, where chairs had been placed for the visitors.

"Now, Miss Sary," Selectman Giddings began in his wheezy voice, "we don't want ye to put on no airs fer us. Jest start out an' run yore school egg-zactly as ye do it every day. Fer a while, that is. After we've seen how ye manage the children, we'll examine them. Eh, Richards? Ain't that right, Jed? Eh?"

His companions nodded assent and settled back in their chairs. Sarah was taken aback for a moment. She had not anticipated this period of classroom work, and she was dubious as to how the selectman would regard her methods. She knew very well that she did not teach in the approved manner. She had injected enthusiasm into study; she had awakened curiosity in her pupils. Instead of sitting like so many bumps on a log, chanting the same lessons over and over, the children had been permitted to study as individuals, each one going ahead as fast as he could. Some of the parents had complained at first, but the results had won them over.

All, that is, but a few diehards like old Silas. However, there was nothing to do but go ahead.

"Very well," Sarah agreed pleasantly and went to stand in front of the children. She bowed her head and the children bowed theirs. They began to recite in unison, "The Lord is my shepherd, I shall not want."

Sarah was aware that the men behind her were listening, not joining in the prayer. She knew why. The children were reciting the beautiful phrases in the reverent, meaningful tones she had taught them to use, not in the singsong chant that was the accepted style.

"I don't care!" she thought rebelliously as the prayer ended. "I know how my brothers and other boys were taught to mumble everything in a monotone. Mother couldn't stand it when she first heard them—and neither could I. Thank goodness I was instructed at home. I avoided forming such miserable habits!"

She could not help glancing at her guests and she saw that Mr. Giddings was frowning. Her heart sank. It would make little difference how well the children recited their lessons. It was she who was being tested—and she had not done well so far.

The selectman, still frowning, took his snuffbox from his vest pocket, and Sarah shuddered at what would follow. There would be no polite covering of mouth and nose with a clean white handkerchief. She had just got this far in her thought when it came: a sneeze so violent that it startled even the expectant children. They heroically smothered their giggles, but Sarah knew that they were teetering on the edge of laughter.

Sarah spoke calmly. "Your slates, please. Row One will recite arithmetic while the rest of you work on the problems assigned yesterday."

She stepped over to the row of older students. From tiny Mary Tucker to big Amasa Leavitt the children were taking out their slates with elaborate precautions against making undue noise. When the slates were all out and the scratching of the pencils against the slick surfaces was the only sound to be heard, Sarah began, "Now did any of you have trouble with yesterday's work?"

Enos Corey looked up and said, "I did. I couldn't get that problem where you said to use the binomial theorem. I tried——"

Sarah smiled. "Yes, I'm sure you did. Who solved it?"

Cora raised her hand.

"Will you explain it to Enos and the class?"

Cora stood up and held her slate for the others to see. She had scarcely opened her mouth to begin the explanation when she was stopped.

"Now, jest a minute there!" Selectman Giddings stepped gingerly down from the platform and came toward Sarah, his gray goatee bristling. "Ye don't mean you're goin' to let that female explain a problem to these boys? That ain't fittin', it ain't! What can a female know about numbers, eh?" He turned to his companions. "Did ye ever hear tell of sech a thing, eh?" he demanded belligerently.

"I don't know," Lew Richards began carefully. "I don't rightly know what that bi-bino—whatever she said—is."

"Well, it must be some sort of numbers. They're supposed to be doin' 'rithmetic. An' I maintain no female has the right or the sense to explain figures to a man!"

Sarah felt irritation mounting in her. She wanted to shout, *Female! Female! What has that got to do with it?* But she knew that any show of temper would be disastrous. She forced herself to smile sweetly and to say diplomatically, "Cora has an unusual mind, sir. She probably inherited her knack from her father: you know how clever with numbers Tom Whiting is."

The old man pondered this for a moment. Then: "Well, I reckon that may be so. Mebbe she did git a bit of sense from Tom. Let her go ahead."

Cora held up her slate again, but before she could say a word, the selectman interrupted once more.

"Say, ain't it mighty quiet in here?" He turned to stare at the children on the other benches, their heads bent over their slates, their pencils busily scratching. The grating screech of pencil on slate was the only sound to be heard.

"What are them childern supposed to be doin', eh? When *I* went to school we conned our lessons out loud, we did. Teacher could hear us blab and knew what we wuz doin'. How can you tell what's goin' on in their heads? How do ye know they're studyin' at all, eh? I don't cotton to sech new-fangled ways. An idle mind, ye know——"

"*Baaaaa! Baaaa!*"

As the impudent sound cut across the old man's jabbering, he stopped, his mouth open in amazement. The children cast quick, frightened glances at each other, then ducked their heads. Sarah felt a shiver run up her spine and into the roots of her hair.

"What's that, eh?" the old man shrilled. "Some smart-alecky——"

"*Baaa! Baaaa! Baaaa!*"

The sound came from the open door. Every head swiveled to look that way, and a titter started among the smaller children and rippled across the room, growing, as it went, into a roar of laughter. For in the doorway stood Mary Tucker's lamb, Snowball, calling for its mistress.

Sarah managed to control her voice. "Mary," she said

quietly, "you forgot to tie Snowball securely. Go out and do so now."

Abashed at being singled out in this way, yet unable to stop her giggling, Mary hesitated a moment before scrambling from her seat and starting toward the lamb. In that brief interval Snowball came into the room, baaing loudly. The children rocked with laughter.

Selectman Giddings saw nothing funny in the interruption. Waving his arms, he ran toward the animal shouting, "Git out! Git out o' here!"

In his impatience he collided with Mary, sending her tumbling against a bench. Sarah hurried to the child, but the old man did not stop. He raised a foot to kick the surprised lamb, and Snowball understood the motion. She turned and fled, her tether rope dragging behind her. Giddings, following and shouting, was at the door when his feet got tangled in the rope and he went sprawling head-first out of the doorway into the damp clay of the yard.

The children were shocked, but they could not control their laughter. Sarah realized that their sudden noise was merely a release from the tension of the morning and she did not try to stop them. She hurried to the selectman as his two companions, themselves grinning broadly, came to his assistance. They got the old man onto his feet and tried to brush off the damp earth that clung to his clothing.

Silas Giddings was seething.

"I'm sorry, sir!" Sarah said earnestly.

"And well ye may be!" the old man sputtered vindictively. "I aim to see that ye don't git another chance to turn our schoolhouse into a sheep pen. I've seen plenty today! Impudent, giggling childern! Females lordin' it over the boys. I don't need to give them younkers any examination. They've showed what they've learned: disrespect, foolishness, scrapin' on slates! If ye'd taught them girls to sew and knit, ye'd have been doin' somethin'—but you're stuck up with book larnin' an' ye want to make all the females jest like yourself! I've said so before an' I say it again!"

Sputtering and muttering, the old man hobbled away, brushing at himself as he went.

Sarah turned helplessly to the other two men. They grinned.

"Don't you worry now, Miss Sarah," Lew Richards said comfortingly. "Don't you worry your pretty head one bit. It wasn't your fault—everyone in town knows how Snowball follows Mary everywhere she goes. We'll see that the true story is told."

Sarah's hazel eyes regarded the man with pleading earnestness. "But I did so want to make a good impression! I love teaching, and these children have so much promise! If I can only have time——"

"You shall, ma'am," Jed Clough promised. "My Jamie's learned to read better 'n his Pa—and in just one winter. Those of us who have children in school want to keep you as teacher. So don't trouble yourself."

Lew Richards nodded. "I guess examination day is over." He chuckled. "Go back inside, Miss Sarah, and let the children have their laugh out."

As the two friendly men left, Sarah returned to the schoolroom. The laughter had stopped now, and the children regarded her with worried faces. They seemed to be saying: *What have we done? We didn't mean to!*

Sarah looked at them a moment and then smiled. "Well," she said cheerfully, "I'll wager that is the very first time an examination came to such an abrupt end!"

Relieved smiles broke out on the faces raised to her.

2

A STRANGE DIPLOMA

ON A SPRING DAY TWO YEARS AFTER THE INTERRUPTED examination, the Buell homestead on East Mountain was bustling with excitement. Young Horatio Gage Buell, Sarah's twenty-two-year-old brother, was due home from Dartmouth College, where he had just been graduated with the class of 1808. Sarah and her mother and father could not keep away from the small square window that looked out upon the road from Newport. And Lottie, the "hired girl" who had been with the Buells ever since Horatio's birth, kept finding excuses to go out into the yard in order to peer down the trail toward town. No one was sure just when Horatio would arrive, for the stagecoach from Hanover was erratic. But one of the Buell horses was waiting at the Newport Inn to carry him home as soon as the stage deposited him in the village.

Sarah was dressed in her best frock, with pleated lace at throat and wrist. She was probably the happiest of the waiting group, for she and her brother had been especially close through the years. It had been Horatio who was responsible for Sarah's advanced education. For while her mother had given all four of her children their early instruction, and very

21

good instruction it had been, it was Horatio who had carried on.

As she peered out the small window, Sarah was remembering the day Horatio first rode down that trail on his way to Dartmouth. How she had longed to go with him! Mingled with her pride in his being accepted at the already noted college had been a deep sorrow that she could not attend a higher school. There was no college for females, and a female would never be admitted to a man's school. Sarah's lips twisted with a humorous quirk at the remembrance.

Seeing his sister's sadness, Horatio had taken her gently in his arms. "Don't you mind, Sally!" he whispered. "I'll teach you everything I learn. When I come home each summer, I'll bring my books and we'll go over everything I've studied during the winter."

"Will you really, Race? Oh, I can hardly wait!" And she had hugged her tall brother convulsively, already bubbling with the thought of the mysterious things that men were taught in their wonderful colleges.

Horatio had been true to his promise. The village of Hanover, where President John Wheelock presided over Dartmouth, was fifty miles to the north. It was a tedious two-day journey by coach, so Horatio could come home only for the long summer vacations. But he had brought with him his books and in those months he had taught Sarah not only history and literature, grammar and composition, but such unusual subjects for a girl as mathematics and Latin. Horatio was a strict but gentle taskmaster. He required Sarah to keep regular school hours and to prepare her lessons meticulously. As a result, at twenty Sarah had a far better education than her contemporaries.

It was due to this superior education that Sarah had kept

her position at the Newport township school. Although old Silas Giddings had never stopped grumbling, the parents had been delighted with the progress made by their children, and her position was assured as long as she wanted it.

And today her beloved brother would be home again, his college life over, ready to start his career as a lawyer. Sarah's heart pounded at the thought. She glanced across the room to where her mother had settled down in an attempt to sew. Though the older woman seemed to be tranquil, Sarah saw her surreptitiously wipe a tear from her eye.

The daughter did not need to ask why. She knew that her mother was thinking that, even with Horatio home, the family was sadly diminished. For tragedy had come to the Buell home during the past year. The beloved oldest son, Charles Whittlesey, had been lost at sea; and the darling of the family, eighteen-year-old Martha Maria, had died of galloping consumption. The two tragedies had suddenly aged the parents, and Sarah sighed as she noted once again the paleness of her mother and the bent form of her father.

He was pacing back and forth now with slow steps, occasionally glancing over Sarah's shoulder to see down the road. Their big farm was too much for him, Sarah thought sadly, and Horatio would not be staying on here to help out. He was to be a lawyer, and he had confided to his sister his secret dream of living in New York City. The family ought to sell the place and move into the village, as they had talked some of doing. Life would be easier, and there would be close friends and neighbors to help distract their minds from their sorrow.

A yell from the road startled Sarah out of her thoughts. She turned quickly to the window and saw horse and rider approaching.

"He's here! He's here!" she cried needlessly, for both parents had heard the shout and were rushing to the door.

Lighter on her feet and swifter than the old people, Sarah was at the horse's side by the time her brother dismounted. He flung his arms about her and laughed down into her hazel eyes, for Horatio was a tall, slender young man, while his sister was so tiny that she barely came to his shoulder.

"Well, well! I'm glad there's a young lady who will welcome me with kisses!" Horatio chuckled.

He then turned to his mother with a gentle tenderness and a look of understanding. He had not been able to come home during her great grief, but she had understood how truly his love had been there. Then he shook hands with his father, saddened at the change in the man.

Covering up their emotion with questions and chatter, they moved into the house. And when Lottie came bustling forward, Horatio gave her a bear hug and a resounding kiss, for the cheerful, buxom woman was regarded as part of the family.

"So you've been graduated!" his father said for the hundredth time.

Horatio grinned. "Yes, sir, Captain Gordon Buell! Your son, Horatio Gates Buell, namesake of the great Revolutionary War hero under whom you served with such distinction, is now prepared to hang out his shingle. He can execute deeds, settle land titles, and, if lucky, earn his own living!"

"Ye talk big!" Lottie said teasingly. "But I ain't going to clap ye on the back till I see that shingle with my own two eyes!"

"That may take some doing, my fine girl!" Horatio chuckled. "For I plan to hang it out some miles from here. But maybe you'll sing a different tune when you see what I brought home with me."

He reached into his carpet bag and brought out a slender roll of parchment. With careful, almost reverent fingers, he unrolled the scroll and held it up for all to see. "My sheepskin!"

Lottie stared at the diploma with its delicately drawn picture of Dartmouth Hall, its flowing scrolls and elaborate lettering. Then, looking up at her hero, who had always brought her some little gift when he came home each year, she said, "That's mighty pretty! Did ye bring me one too?"

The quartet of listeners managed to hide their smiles as he answered seriously, "I brought you something prettier and probably much more useful. But before I get it out for you—I did bring a diploma home for Sarah."

Now the group could smile without reserve. Sarah cried, "You're teasing, Race!"

"I am not. I'm in deadly earnest!" Horatio reached into the carpet bag again and brought out another slender scroll. It looked much like the sheepskin, but Sarah could see that it was really heavy, creamy paper. He held the roll out to her and she took it, unrolling it with trembling fingers.

"I reckoned Sarah had finished college work the same as I had done and was as entitled as I to a diploma. I couldn't convince President Wheelock— Fact is, I didn't even try to— but I did the next best."

Sarah held up the paper. On it, copied almost exactly, were the embellishments on the real diploma, with some differences. Instead of Dartmouth Hall, there was a sketch of the Buell farmhouse, and where the words DARTMOUTH COLLEGE should be was an elaborately inscribed HORATIO GATES BUELL COLLEGE. This institution conferred upon

Sarah Josepha Buell the degree of Mistress of Arts, *summa cum laude!* Giggling, but with eyes bright with tears, Sarah looked up at her brother.

"Oh Race, I'll treasure this all my life! You were a darling to think of it. Thank you, thank you."

Now Horatio brought out other gifts: a shawl for his mother, a book for his father, and a bright neckerchief for Lottie.

"Well now!" Captain Buell beamed. He had never relinquished his Revolutionary War title. "Well now! This calls for a celebration. Lottie, haven't we something for a special tea? I think I smelled crullers cooking this morning."

"Yes, sir. I'll set it out in no time!" Lottie said and bustled out of the room.

Later, when Horatio and Sarah were alone together for a few minutes, the brother voiced the thought that had been troubling him ever since he arrived. "It's Pa, Sally! You must have seen how bent he is . . ."

Sarah nodded. "Yes, I know. The farm is too much for him."

"It always was!" Horatio said glumly. "Four hundred acres of rocky mountainside. I don't see why he ever accepted it from Grandpa Dan!"

"Oh yes, you do know why, Race. Ma and Pa had nothing when they got married. The war had broken Pa's health. He had won honors, of course—*Captain* Gordon Buell! Ma was so proud to be chosen by him. But he had lost his health and had no money——"

"Yes, I understand all that. But Pa was never cut out to be a farmer and this place was not really fit for a farm."

Sarah smiled and patted her brother's arm. "He's made a living for us all—and a good living too," she reminded him. "Of course it was hard for both Ma and Pa. But we've always had plenty of food, and what is more important—plenty of books. Being sort of isolated up here, Ma had time to teach us a lot. And though you and Charley did suffer in public school, it didn't hurt you too much because you had Ma's teaching at home. If it weren't for Pa's health, I'd say we've been very fortunate in having Grandpa Buell's gift."

"You're right, as usual," Horatio agreed. "But maybe living in Hanover these past years has made me a bit impatient with the isolated life here. Seriously, Sally, I think we ought to sell the farm and move down to Newport."

"I've thought so too—and even sort of hinted at it," Sarah confessed. "In fact, Pa has more or less come around to that idea, I think. He talks about moving to the village and opening a tavern there. You know there's quite a lot of travel on the road from Keene to Hanover now. And with Henry Schoolcraft building a glass factory at Keene, there'll be more. All of northwest New Hampshire will be wanting his bottles and glassware. And the drovers reach Newport the second night——"

"You've figured it all out, I see."

"I think Pa has. He's even mentioned the name he'd choose if he had a tavern: *The Rising Sun* . . ."

"Well, let's hope he carries out his plans. Maybe I can help, if he sells the farm while I'm home this summer. I could help in the moving, help him pick out a site in the village——"

A smile dimpled Sarah's cheeks. "He's already picked a site, right on the main road, of course."

Horatio grinned down at his sister. "Well, all that's left for the noble son to do is to tag along with plans already made."

"And put his noble shoulder to the wheel now and then!" Sarah added.

3

HAPPY INTERLUDE

ENCOURAGED AND PROMPTED BY SARAH AND HORATIO, Captain Buell finally sold the farmstead and moved to Newport. There he carried out his dream and opened *The Rising Sun* Tavern on the main road from Keene to Hanover. By 1811 he was prospering as he had scarcely hoped to do. And Sarah, still teaching the township school, no longer had to ride down the mountainside in all sorts of weather.

One autumn day in that same year as Sarah was walking home from school she noticed a new sign on one of the buildings on Main Street

DAVID HALE
ATTORNEY

Sarah smiled. Newport needed an attorney and she had hoped that Horatio would relinquish his exciting life in New York City and come back here to fill that need. But Horatio seemed to have outgrown the small town, and now someone else had arrived.

28

As Sarah passed the office under the small sign, she tried to peer into the window without seeming to stare. She could see nothing but a huge desk and a battered chair. She walked on slowly.

"I don't know why I'm curious about him," she murmured to herself. "He's probably some withered old codger who hates women schoolteachers."

She sighed. She was lonely. Her life was pleasant enough within the narrow circle of home and school and church, but it was far from exciting. She had no close companions of her own age, and there was scant possibility of her ever having any. The village girls were married long before they were Sarah's age. At twenty-three she was on her way to becoming an old maid in the eyes of her neighbors. She seemed to be settled in the role of teacher, where she could stay till eyesight and hearing failed, until her first pupils were grandparents, until her usefulness was ended.

As for the young men of Newport, she shrugged. The men she knew had little hankering for book learning, and they shyly regarded Sarah with a mixture of awe and impatience. For many months after moving to Newport she had tried to be friendly, to find some common interests with the young men she met at church socials. She had even helped her father in the tavern when her loneliness became too acute. But these efforts had done no good. The young men were afraid of her, and she was annoyed at their lack of respect for learning—and for women. Sarah could not meekly accept the local contempt for the "female" mind that threw the women of the village into a position definitely inferior to that of the men.

Walking slowly along the grass-bordered walk that afternoon, with dry leaves fluttering down from the wind-shaken trees, Sarah felt more lonely than ever. "It's that attorney's sign," she told herself. "It made me think of Race. Race! Race! Why aren't there more men like you? Men who care what a woman thinks—who know that a woman has a mind, a personality that is as valuable, as precious as their own?"

Unaccustomed tears were very close to the surface as she pushed open the tavern door and stepped inside. It was too early for many customers, and she often cut through this way to the living quarters at the rear.

Coming in out of the autumn sunlight, Sarah did not notice that a guest was at the far side of the room talking with her father. Captain Buell called out to her:

"Daughter, come here. I want our new lawyer to meet you."

Sarah walked toward the two men.

"Sarah," her father said, "let me present Attorney David Hale. Mr. Hale, this is my daughter. She teaches the township school here."

Sarah's hand was clasped in firm, strong fingers. She raised her lashes and looked into a young and handsome face, with brown eyes that twinkled down at her. Instantly she felt his friendliness and warmth; she was more at ease with this stranger than she ever had been with any of the village boys.

From that moment the two were friends, and before the year was out the village gossips were nodding their heads. Miss Sarah had at last caught herself a beau, they murmured. There'd be a wedding before long.

The gossips had many months of waiting, however, while David established a remunerative law practice and built a home for his bride.

Utilizing the privilege of her long service in the family, Lottie undertook to give Sarah some advice.

"Don't you act uppity with that young man," she said darkly. "Don't you make him wait till he has a house and everything fancy for you. You're not getting any younger, you know!"

Sarah smiled. She could afford to treat Lottie's remarks with cheerful candor. "I'm not making him wait, Lottie—I'd marry him tomorrow. But David is the cautious kind. He wants to have a home for me, and a practice that will enable him to afford a servant and a carriage——"

Lottie shook her head, her expression grim. "In other words, he's going to treat you like a queen. Well, you deserve it, I guess. But it ain't natural."

Sarah was happy, and she knew her happiness shone in her like a lighted lamp. She was not at all vain, but she could not help seeing what her mirror revealed—that her happiness had given her a new beauty. Her large hazel eyes glowed; her chestnut hair gleamed as if burnished; her pale, oval face had new color.

"I'm not beautiful!" she sometimes whispered to her reflection, "but I *look* beautiful. Oh David, it is all because of you!"

At long last the village dames were satisfied. In the fall of 1813, two years after meeting David, Sarah announced the date of her wedding. At twenty-five Miss Sarah was to give up the school she had taught for seven years. With mixed emotions Sarah considered the step she was taking. There was no hesitancy, only eager acquiescence. But the school . . .

"Are you going to miss it too much?" David asked. And when Sarah slowly shook her head he went on, "Well, the children will miss you. I know there's not another school in New Hampshire—I'll make that the whole United States— where the children have been taught Latin and mathematics and history and logic. Boys and girls alike!"

"Only a smattering of these things, David. I'd hate to have a Dartmouth professor examine them——"

"Naturally. They're just children. But the girls you have taught would probably put the wives of those very professors to shame."

"I've taught the girls exactly the same as the boys," Sarah admitted. "To me, a girl's mind is as capable as a boy's. And I must confess that I rather hate seeing my school taken over by someone else. I wouldn't give it up for anyone but you, David."

Horatio, who was now married, and his wife came up from New York City for the wedding. Sarah took them to see her new home, "Lawyer Hale's Mansion," on Main Street.

"Isn't it beautiful, Race?" she asked happily. "The village green is right in front of it, like a park. From the windows I can see everything that goes on . . ."

Her brother nodded. It was a lovely house, large and square and white, with a row of six windows upstairs and four down. The doorway in the center was crowned by an exquisite fanlight.

"It certainly looks as if 'lawyering' in Newport pays well!" Horatio said admiringly.

"Wait till you see inside," Sarah told him. "It's all furnished and waiting for us."

She led him through the door into a wide hall that ran toward the back, where the door to the kitchen centered the rear wall. Sarah turned through the first door on her right.

"This is our family room," she said proudly, "the old New England 'keeping' room. Isn't it lovely?"

Horatio looked about with appraising eyes. The floor was of broad pine boards, the wainscoting was blue and the upper walls and ceiling a gleaming white. David had paid a traveling artist to paint a grove of trees on the white walls, which gave the room a feeling of spaciousness and coolness and seclusion that no store-bought wallpaper could provide. On one side of the room was a wide fireplace, above which was painted a golden eagle. Around the bird's head was a halo of stars, and clasped in his talons was an olive branch and a sheaf of arrows.

Horatio smiled. "That eagle," he said gently. "You'd be bound to have it where you can see it every time you raise your eyes."

"It is the symbol of our country," Sarah answered. "Both David and I want it always before us."

"It is a perfect room for you, Sally," her brother went on. His eyes rested on the wide, chintz-covered sofa, the shelves filled with books, the comfortable chairs. "I hope you spend a lifetime of happy hours here."

"David and I plan to spend our evenings together in this room. You remember, Race, how you used to make me keep regular hours of study at home? Well, David and I are going to put in two hours every evening, from eight to ten o'clock, studying together. He can teach me so much. Since I've known him I've discovered that my style of writing is too sentimental, too florid. He will help me to improve that—and many other things too!"

Her brother smiled down affectionately into his sister's eyes. "What a passion you have for improvement, Sally! And you are so perfect just as you are."

"No! No one is ever perfect, Race, never complete. And learning is so exciting—I hope I never stop."

The months after the wedding flew by swiftly and happily. Sarah and David were able to carry out their plans with unusual success. The hours of evening study were held inviolate, and Sarah found, as she had told her brother, that David's criticism, gentle and kindly as it was, was helping her to overcome faults in expression and understanding.

Their first child, David Emerson, was born on February 15, 1815. He was followed in May, two years later, by a tiny brother whom they named Horatio, after Sarah's brother. But in spite of these interruptions, the study hours continued.

The first break in the pleasant schedule came late in the summer of 1818. Sarah had never quite regained her strength after little Horatio's birth, and now, just as the baby was beginning to walk and another child was expected in the spring, Sarah's health failed seriously.

"She has quick consumption," the doctor told David, shaking his head sadly. "I don't need to tell you what that means."

David's throat ached. No, the doctor didn't need to explain. It meant that he would not have Sarah much longer. So many people, especially women, were dying of this illness —a disease so rapid in its tragic effect that it was called "galloping consumption." It was this dreaded ailment that had killed Sarah's sister, Martha Maria, when she was only eighteen.

"I can't tell her," he muttered.

"I think she knows," Dr. Allen replied. "I'm sure she knows, David."

David returned to the sitting room, where his wife lay on the wide sofa. He picked up the book he had been reading aloud to her, and tried to go on with the story but his voice failed. He swallowed with difficulty, then, suddenly closing the book, he laid it on the table and without a word left the room.

She watched him go, knowing what the doctor must have told him. She wanted to reassure him, but there was nothing she could say. Her death was approaching, and they both knew it. She closed her eyes wearily and lay still, too weak to rise and follow her husband, too ill to give him the comfort she knew he needed. 1185114

It was dark when David returned. Mahala, the servant girl who had been with them since their marriage, had lighted one lamp on the table by David's chair. It made a little golden pool of light in which the familiar chair stood bravely, but the sofa where Sarah lay was in shadow. David strode across the room and knelt down beside his wife. With strong arms he gathered her close.

"You're not going to die," he whispered. "I won't let you!"

Sarah ran her pale fingers through David's thick dark hair. "Of course, darling," she agreed softly.

"I have a plan," David went on eagerly. "Tomorrow I'll send for my sister Hannah. We'll leave little David and Horatio here with her. Then I am going to take you on a trip—it came to me just now. What you need is rest and fresh air. I'll put you in the buggy and we'll go gypsying, just we two—over the hills. They're beautiful now. We'll sleep out-of-doors; we'll take in all the fresh air and pure mountain water your frail body can hold. We'll work a miracle . . ."

The very next day David put his plan into action. His sister Hannah was delighted to take over the lovely house and the two jolly little boys. David hitched Dapple into the two-wheeled gig and put in a rucksack of clothing and a roll of bedding. Then he carried Sarah out and placed her, carefully wrapped and bolstered by pillows, on the seat. They waved good-by to the boys and set out.

As they passed Dr. Allen's house, David drew rein and the doctor came out to see who had stopped at the gate.

He was appalled at seeing Sarah. "What harebrained trick is this?" he demanded harshly. When David had explained his plan the physician shook his head. "You'll never bring her home alive."

David's eyes were somber, but his voice was confident. "I have thought it all out, Doctor. If, as you say, she has only a short time to live, I want it to be a happy, carefree time—with me. But you are wrong. I'll bring her back, well!"

David and Sarah traveled slowly over the New Hampshire hills, gloriously lovely in their autumn colors of russet and gold and brown. David kept his eyes on his wife's face, watching for any sign that she was growing weaker, any hint of the danger that loomed so close. One golden afternoon, Sarah caught sight of a cluster of wild grapes, turned purple by the previous night's frost. "Oh David!" she cried. "Frost grapes! Let's stop and pick some!"

David stopped the gig and lifted Sarah down. She almost ran to the old tree stump over which the grapevine clambered. Laughing with excitement, she reached out and plucked a bunch of the small purple fruit. David's heart contracted with sudden happiness. The laugh was clear and sweet—the sweetest music he had ever heard.

Sarah dropped down on a hummock of grass and devoured the fruit with a zest she had shown for no other food. David watched her thoughtfully, eating his own grapes more slowly.

"Aren't they good, David! I've never tasted anything so good."

From that day on, they searched the hillsides for wild grapes, and Sarah ate them as if she could never get enough. Day by day color came into her cheeks, laughter to her lips, happiness and health to her lovely eyes.

Six weeks from the day they had paused at Dr. Allen's gate, they stopped there again. The doctor came out as before, but this time his ruddy face showed not apprehension but amazement.

"It's a miracle, David!" he cried. "How did you do it?"

"Love, fresh air, and grapes," David said, chuckling.

Sarah's slim hand rested on her husband's arm. "And the greatest of these . . . ," she whispered softly. Her eyes told David the rest: ". . . is love."

4

TRAGEDY STRIKES

AFTER SARAH AND DAVID RETURNED HOME FROM THEIR "gypsying," Aunt Hannah stayed on to help manage the house and give her sister-in-law more time to spend with the little boys. Sarah still kept sacred her two hours of study with David each evening, and the winter passed by uneventfully. In March her first daughter, Frances Ann, was born. A year and a half later, in December of 1820, another daughter, Sarah Josepha, joined the family.

Sarah was delighted with her children. She made up little verses to sing to them and games and finger-plays to teach them. She began instructing her babies as soon as they showed any awareness of the world about them.

> "Thumbkin bold,
> Next man to hold,
> Longman,
> Weak Man,
> And Mamma's wee Dan!"

she would sing, showing baby Josepha each finger on her plump little hand.

Or to Horatio, dressing himself,

"Sixty seconds make a minute—
Time to tie my shoe.
Sixty minutes make an hour—
See how much I can do."

One day a neighbor paused at the gate to watch Sarah playing with her children. "What a pretty family!" she exclaimed. "Two boys and two females."

Sarah's response was unwontedly sharp. "Two boys and two girls!"

The other woman bridled, "Well, I never!" she declared and walked on.

Sarah cuddled her daughters. "I won't permit you to be called females!" she murmured against Frances Ann's dark hair. "That word somehow classes you with animals, not human beings. You are little girls, my daughters, and some-day you will be women. But never females!"

David's law practice thrived. Now, besides Hannah and Mahala, there was a yard man to help with the garden and the horses, and keep the buggy shining. Sarah was able to spend most of her day with the children. She had very definite ideas about their training and instruction, even though the neighbors looked askance at the precocity of Lawyer Hale's offspring. But even after all these years, the two evening hours were saved for David and Sarah's study together.

It was because he wished to reach home in time for supper with his family and those two precious hours with his wife that David rode through a sudden, fierce storm late one September afternoon in 1822. He had been called to New-bury on business and had decided to travel on horseback. Having finished his business there, he started home, taking a short cut trail across the northern slope of Mount Sunapee. And there the storm struck, sleet and hail and bitter wind whipping against the lone rider. David kept doggedly on.

By the time he reached home, he was wet to the skin. Levi, the handy man, came running to take care of the horse, and David climbed stiffly from the saddle. He went into the big kitchen and over to the fireplace, where Mahala was preparing the evening meal. His teeth were chattering.

At the sound of her husband's entrance, Sarah ran into the kitchen. She was shocked at David's appearance.

"You're chilled through!" she cried. "Come, David, get those wet clothes off, and put on something warm and dry." She laid her cool palm against his flushed cheek. "You're feverish—but shivering. My dear, I'm afraid you're really ill. You must get to bed at once."

Hannah, attracted by the sounds, came and peered at her brother. Then, without comment, she went to the door and sent Levi for Dr. Allen.

Sarah was frightened, but she kept her voice calm and her hands steady as she helped David into the big feather bed. He was shaking uncontrollably and muttering about a pain in his chest. When Dr. Allen arrived, there was no hesitation in his diagnosis:

"He's taken a violent chill, and he's run down from working so hard. We'll have to be careful or pneumonia will set in."

Though they did everything they could, pneumonia did set in. Sarah would not leave her husband's bedside. She nursed him with desperate calmness, praying silently all the time that his life would be spared. But within a week David was dead.

Sarah was prostrated with grief, and Hannah assumed full charge of all the necessary sad details. And two weeks after David's death Sarah's fifth child, William George, was born.

Neighbors and relatives hastened to offer assistance and advice. There were many friendly offers to take the children into their homes. Sarah could not bear to think of being parted from her babies.

"Oh Hannah," she cried, "I can't let them go—not even one of them. I know these people mean well, but I must keep my children."

Hannah nodded. "I know, I know. We'll manage somehow."

"I know they think I can't bring the children up, alone as I am," Sarah said sadly. She was well aware that it was the usual thing for generous friends to take the children of a widow so that the mother could be free to go into domestic service. That was about the only work possible for a woman —that and dressmaking.

Sarah and Hannah sat together now during those two empty evening hours, trying to plan the future. They knew what the neighbors were thinking: *"Tch-tch!* It's too bad Lawyer Hale put so much money into that big house. Too bad he gave his wife and children all those high-toned ideas. If he'd put his money away!"

Sarah grew angry when she heard of such comments. How dare anyone criticize David? Of course he had denied them nothing. He was prospering, but he was still young and had not had enough years behind him to lay away much. He had not dreamed—none of them had dreamed—that he would die so young.

She told Hannah, "I don't mind poverty for myself. Nothing can add to my grief, and nothing could take from it. But I do not want our children to be deprived of the things necessary for a happy, healthy life. And an education! That is what I fear most—that the children may be unable to have a proper education."

"We'll think of something," Hannah said firmly.

They finally decided to open a millinery shop in one room of the big house. They could do the work and still keep the children with them. With whatever scanty funds Sarah could scrape up, as well as some help from David's brother Masons, Hannah went to Boston and purchased a supply of bonnet shapes, flowers, feathers, and ribbons. With high hopes they placed a sign in the window and let it be known among the villagers that they would supply the latest styles and most attractive bonnets at modest prices.

It was a doomed project. Neither Sarah nor Hannah had any talent for millinery work, and day by day, week by week, they faced the bitter fact that they were not making enough to live on.

For years Sarah had been writing verse. In the happy days with David her poems had been gay and cheerful. In the sad days after his death, writing proved the only consolation she could find. Sarah found that in poetry she could express her grief and loneliness.

One day a friend of David's came to see how Sarah was getting along. This friend had been elected to David's position as Worshipful Master of the Corinthian Lodge of Free and Accepted Masons, a position of honor that David had held only a few months before his death. Now the visitor glanced around the room at the stacks of unattractive, unsold bonnets. He looked carefully at Sarah, whose eyes were ringed with dark circles of worry and sleeplessness.

"I'm afraid you're not very happy as a milliner, Mrs. Hale," he said gently. "We must find something more to your liking. Can't you think of something—anything at all—that you'd rather do than make bonnets?"

Sarah glanced at the work table, where a sheet of paper

lay. She had been penning a verse instead of trimming a bonnet.

"I would rather write," she said ruefully. "But I cannot earn a living for myself and family that way."

"Why not!" her visitor exclaimed. "What do you write anyway?"

Sarah began hesitantly, "Only verse . . ."

"That's it! That's the very thing! A book of verse—can you give me enough for a book? We'll have every Mason in New England purchase a copy! Your husband did a great deal for the Corinthian Lodge, and this will be our chance to show our appreciation."

Sarah could not smother the thrill of hope that stirred in her. "Is it possible . . . ?" she asked slowly.

"Anything is possible!" the man declared. "You get to work, collect what you have written—write others if necessary. I'll come back in a week or two and see what you have."

For the first time since David's death Sarah seemed to glimpse a bit of happiness. She hated millinery work and had neglected it often to scribble her verses. Now, if only the thing she loved to do could be made to pay! Hands trembling with excitement, Sarah went through her old notebooks, selecting the poems she thought were best. She had been working, at intervals, on a long poem that she had intended to call "The Genius of Oblivion." Now she went over this carefully, revising and correcting; adding lines here and there; deleting those she thought imperfect. With this long poem and a score of shorter verses, she had what she considered enough for a small volume.

When her friend returned to pick up the verses, he was delighted. "I've found a publisher. Jacob Moore of Concord has promised to publish the book. Now have you written the dedication and everything?"

"Yes. I've dedicated it, of course, to David."

He took the sheaf of papers, written in Sarah's small, tight script, and thumbed through them. "It looks as if you have some very good material here." He beamed. He turned back to the dedication, and his face grew serious as he read Sarah's frank statement of why the little book was being launched and her plea to the public:

And lives there one, who, with ungen'rous part
Will spurn this offering of the broken heart!

It was with mingled pride and trepidation that Sarah finally held in her hands her first book, which appeared in 1823. It was a tiny volume, bound in tan leather, the proud title almost too much for the small dimensions of the cover. *The Genius of Oblivion and Other Original Poems* by a "Lady of New Hampshire."

"Will it mean anything? Will people like it? Have I the talent necessary to be a writer?" she asked Hannah. "I know the poets—the great poets. I know how good they are. But I—well, the verses are honest expressions, at any rate. I can say that much for them. But I'm afraid!"

Hannah, who did not have Sarah's familiarity with literature, was ecstatic. "It's wonderful! You are a poet, not a milliner. From now on you must devote your time to writing. I'll muddle along with the bonnets."

The little book had a far better sale than Sarah had dared to hope. She knew that this was largely due to the loyal support of David's brother Masons. But even so, to earn money by writing rather than by sewing or millinery was so much more pleasant.

"I'm going to try a novel," she told Hannah, feeling very daring.

Her sister-in-law gaped at her. "Whatever put such an

idea into your head? Poetry, yes. That's fine and appropriate for a woman to do. But a novel! There aren't many men who can write a whole book like that—and I don't think any woman ever did."

Sarah nibbled thoughtfully at the end of her quill pen. "You may be right, Hannah, as far as American women go. But English women have written novels. I've just been reading Fanny Burney's *Camilla*. And long ago, when I was still quite young, I read Mrs. Radcliffe's *Mysteries of Udolpho*. How I shivered over the horrrifying events! And how proud I was, even then, that a woman had written that story. Anyway, if American men write novels—Mr. James Fenimore Cooper is said to be making money with his novel, *The Spy*—I don't see why a woman can't, if she tries."

Hannah was still doubtful, but she said loyally, "Well, I daresay that if you set your mind to it, you can do it, Sarah. I'll take over more work to give you time . . ."

"Oh Hannah, you are a treasure! How much I owe to David—those years of perfect happiness, the children, and you!"

So, in between making bonnets now and then and supervising the children's education—for Sarah would not send them to the public school—she set to work on her novel.

"I want to put into it all the things David and I talked about—the differences between the North and South—the differing ways of life, and attitudes toward such things as slavery. But I want to point out that these very differences should bind us close together, one nation—one unique nation. I'm going to call it *A New England Tale*, for it will be laid here; but I hope to make it a wholly American story, showing our ideas and ideals, our way of life. Perhaps, a century from now, others will read it and get a glimpse of life today."

Hannah listened, wide-eyed. "Mercy! I don't see how you can ever get all of that into one book. But take your time, Sarah. Make it just the way you want it."

Sarah took her time—three years—to write the book. As it progressed she read chapters aloud to Hannah, who marveled at the astute observations and comments of her sister-in-law.

"It's a great book, Sarah!" Hannah declared. "The whole world will want to read it!"

"I think it's much better than my little book of verse," Sarah admitted. "I do hope it has some meaning for the world. Maybe, when people in the North and people in the South read it, they will feel that the two sections of the country are not so different after all. We are all Americans— all loyal to one flag."

"You worry so much about that, Sarah! I don't imagine it's too important."

Sarah frowned, troubled. "Maybe not now, Hannah. But unless the two sections stop finding fault with each other, it might be important. Dreadfully important. Maybe if they come to understand each other—if my book will help to achieve that—I'll be content."

Northwood, A New England Tale, was published in December, 1827. This time her book was put out by a Boston publishing house—Bowles and Dearborn. The novel was printed in two small leatherbound volumes and, rather to Sarah's surprise, it was a tremendous success. Never before had any writer attempted a novel dealing with the differences between the North and the South. Never had anyone written a book presenting the problem of having slaves in one section of the country while they were not tolerated in another section. Sarah's daring themes caused a sensation. Her book was in every home, talked about at every gathering. English publishers rushed into print with *Northwood*. On the Continent, German and French editions appeared.

"You're famous, Sarah!" Hannah cried exultingly.

Sarah eyed her first royalty check with disbelief. "Whoever thought I could make so much money doing something so pleasant as writing?"

Letters began to pour in upon the author. Sarah stared at them, wondering why so many people took the time to write to her, an unknown. One day shortly after *Northwood* had appeared at the bookstalls, she unfolded a letter that had a businesslike look. She scanned it rapidly at first, then again, more slowly. Excitement churned through her.

"Hannah!" she cried. "What do you think? This is a letter from a Mr. Putnam, in Boston. He wants me to come there and edit a magazine for women. A magazine for women, Hannah! What a wonderful idea, what a challenge. Dare I accept it?"

"You can do anything you put your mind to, Sarah," Hannah declared.

"But this is something so new—so different. He says the ideas I expressed in *Northwood* show that I have a keen understanding of women's possibilities—and he's been thinking that women should have a magazine of their own. He says he had never found anyone that he felt could edit such a magazine until he read my novel. Then he felt he had found the person he had been searching for. Oh Hannah, what a wonderful tribute!"

She paused, her cheeks flushed, her hazel eyes bright with excitement. After a moment she spoke again, slowly and carefully:

"What would David advise me to do? I'm certain, Hannah, that he would say 'Go and God be with you.' I'm going to accept this offer. I shall write Mr. Putnam now . . . . before my qualms make me change my mind."

======o═o══════ 5

A NEW LIFE

WHEN ANY DOUBTS ROSE IN SARAH'S MIND CONCERNING
this challenging adventure, she crushed them with enthusiastic thoughts of what she could do with a magazine
published especially for women. It was such a daring idea!
No one in America had ever before tried a magazine addressed only to women. As far as Sarah knew, no one in the
world had ever tried so revolutionary a project. But how
practical! Half the world was made up of women. Their
spheres of action, needs, and interests were different from
men's. Why should they not have a magazine of their own?

And yet, in the wakeful hours of night, fears did arise.
On her next birthday she would be forty, an age when
women were considered old and through with the excitement and adventures of life. She had never even visited a
city as large as Boston. She had never had any experience at
all at editing anything and, of course, had no idea of what a
woman's magazine should be. In addition to all this, she was
a widow with five children. Young David was not yet thir-
teen and little William only five. She would have to dispose

49

of her property here in Newport, move her entire family to Boston, rent a house, arrange for the care of her children, and take over a new kind of work. Could she manage all this?

Staring into the darkness, Sarah whispered, "David, help me." She recalled the conversations they had held of an evening, and went over the ideas she had expounded in *Northwood*. And she knew that, frightened or not, inexperienced as she was, she must accept the challenge presented to her.

In order to give herself no time to "back out," Sarah had written immediately to John Putnam in Boston accepting his offer. She set to work at once settling her scanty affairs in Newport and preparing to move her family to Boston. Hannah, loyal as she was, could not see her way clear to accompany her sister-in-law.

Sarah arrived in the strange city one wintry December day in 1827, with her children clustered about her, each hugging a bulky bundle of possessions. Drawing on unknown reserves of efficiency, she found a respectable boardinghouse, settled the children in young David's care, and set out to meet her first employer.

She found John Putnam to be a genial person whose fascination with *Northwood* had convinced him that Sarah was a most capable and reliable "editress."

"I want to publish our first issue next month—start the new year right!" he declared. "I'll leave everything up to you, Mrs. Hale. After reading your novel I was positive that you are a woman with advanced ideas—and that's what we'll need to make so revolutionary a publication succeed."

Sarah nodded thoughtfully. "I've been thinking about this ever since your letter came, and I believe that our first problem will be winning over the men——"

"Men?" Putnam interrupted. "We're not aiming at them. We're after female readers."

Sarah shrank involuntarily at the hated word, but she went on firmly. "Of course, sir. But how many women have the money or the liberty to subscribe to a magazine? It will be their husbands or fathers who pay the bill—and who give permission for their wives or daughters to read our publication. We must, first of all, convince the men that they will gain—not lose—by having their wives subscribe."

The publisher beamed. "You're right, absolutely right! I feel more every minute that you are the one and only woman in this country with the foresight and acumen to edit my new magazine."

If the first issue was to come out in January, Sarah saw that she must lose no time. But first of all, she must find a place to live and see that her children would be properly cared for while she was at the office. She set out with the new energy and determination that had been released by the challenge of the Boston offer. She soon found a suitable house near enough to a public school for the older boys and close to one of the new small schools for girls. Sarah's investigation showed that both were superior to most of the common schools and that she could safely entrust her children to their instruction.

Five-year-old William was still too young for school, though under his mother's instruction he had acquired far more knowledge than other children his age. Sarah made inquiries and soon found an intelligent young woman who was eager to instruct William in Mrs. Hale's home and care for him during his mother's absence. However, she had had no experience in teaching.

"That doesn't matter," Sarah assured her. "I will guide you. I have very definite ideas on how children should be taught, and if you will follow my directions, you will have no trouble at all. I should like William to have companions his own age, and I thought that we could work out a program whereby this could be accomplished and you could be paid. At present I cannot afford, myself, to pay you," Sarah explained frankly. "You may use this large front room as a classroom, rent-free, in exchange for William's instruction and care. Then you may bring in other children, charging a reasonable fee, and thus make your work profitable. What do you say?"

The young woman was agreeable, the details were settled, and Sarah thus established in her home the very first classes for pre-school children.

Now she turned her attention to the first edition of the *Ladies' Magazine*. At her desk in the small, cluttered office of Putnam and Hunt at 41 Washington Street, Sarah stared down at the blank piece of paper in front of her and wondered what she could put in that first issue. There was no backlog of material, of course, and no "stable" of authors to call upon. She must provide every word. If she could not discover suitable articles or stories, she must write them herself. She faced the problem bravely but anxiously.

Well, she thought, first things first. I must write an introduction explaining what the magazine is and what it hopes to do.

Remembering that she must win over the men, who would have to pay for the magazine, Sarah wrote carefully:

"In this age of innovation, perhaps no experiment will have an influence more important on the character and happiness of our society, than the granting to women . . ." She paused there and looked again at the word "women." How good it seemed to use it. And yet how startling it would be to the readers, who seldom saw and still more seldom used the word. If she wished to conciliate the men, she must not startle them. They were not used to the word, and their reaction might be that they wanted nothing to do with a magazine so revolutionary as to replace the familiar terms with newfangled ones. She crossed out the word "women" and substituted "female."

She continued: ". . . . than the granting to females the advantages of a systematic and thorough education. The honor of this triumph in favor of intellect over long-established prejudices belongs to the men of America."

She smiled shrewdly. That ought to please them. And now to assure them that they have nothing to fear from the new journal—that we are not going to incite their wives and daughters to rebellion, but will encourage them to be docile and thrifty and obedient.

She went on writing, her eyes serious, but her mobile lips curved in a gentle smile. She promised the men that there would never be anything in the magazine that would cause their womenfolk to be less eager to do their household work and to take care of the men. And there would never be anything that would encourage the females to try to take over the duties and authority of the men:

"There will never be anything in our pages that the men cannot read, and we invite the husbands and fathers to study each issue so they will know at firsthand the value this journal will be to their families."

Sarah paused, rereading what she had written. Had she sounded properly meek and dependent? Perhaps it wouldn't hurt to add a direct plea—men liked to be chivalrous. They liked to respond generously to a woman's cry for help. Many wives would be afraid to ask their husbands for money to subscribe to a magazine of their own. She would have to ask for them. She dipped the quill pen into the inkpot and added, "Will not the husband, the father, the brother, the lover subscribe to this . . ."

So much for the men! If this appeal didn't win them, nothing would. But the women must be won over too. They might hesitate about reading a magazine directed at them unless they knew what it would contain. Sarah felt that she knew exactly what women—American women—would want, and, more especially, what they needed to read. So she promised them stories and poems and articles on all phases of women's activity. And she promised herself that in the columns she controlled she would battle fiercely for the acceptance of women as the mental equals of men.

Who else is there that I must conciliate? she thought. Her smooth brow wrinkled in a frown of concentration. I don't want to set this little ship asail under a storm of protest and indignation. It is bound to have enough difficulty without that. So perhaps I'd better say something to the rival publishers, who will certainly not welcome a new competitor for the little money spent on magazines.

A little timidly, she added a note to reassure the publishers of other magazines that this new venture did not intend to compete with established magazines. "But," she concluded, "surely those editors will not frown upon this attempt because it is unprecedented, or endeavor to perplex the task of one already trembling for the issue of an enterprise upon which she has reluctantly engaged."

John Putnam, reading this introduction, grinned. "You are quite the diplomat, buttering up the men like this."

Sarah flushed faintly. "I am not insincere," she replied somewhat primly. "I simply realize that men cannot bear to help a woman who shows the least sign of strength or the slightest opposition to their assumed supremacy. The only way to enlist their support is to show that you need it, that you depend upon them. A woman must be gentle——"

"The iron hand in the velvet glove," Putnam remarked quietly.

There was scant material to draw upon for this first issue. Sarah had read a report of a lecture given by the Reverend Charles Burroughs dealing with female education. The Rector of St. John's Episcopal Church favored broadening the scope of education for women, so Sarah obtained his permission to publish the speech. She found a couple of poems that suited her. And that was all from outside. Sarah wrote all the other articles, stories, and poems in this first issue. It was a tremendous task, and her quill pen had to be sharpened and resharpened as she scribbled furiously till late into the night. But she had enough manuscript copy for the first issue of the small magazine ready in time.

It was with a feeling of relief, tempered with trepidation, that she delivered the last sheet of foolscap, covered with her writing, to the compositor. She did not apologize for her slanting script, difficult as it was to read with the *r*'s and *i*'s and *n*'s and *u*'s scarcely distinguishable from one another. She knew that the compositor was accustomed to deciphering handwriting much worse than her own. And she intended to read the proofs carefully to catch any mistakes he might make.

New as she was to the job, Sarah wanted to learn all she could about the printing of a magazine. She went out into the shop and watched the "typos" as they plucked the letters from the fonts and placed them in the forms. It was all done by hand, but the men worked so rapidly that Sarah was fascinated.

Each page of the magazine was laid out on the new, lever-operated flatbed press. Then one of the workmen took up the ink-balls—sticks with inked balls of felt on one end—and with these he inked the form. Then he laid a blank sheet of paper on it, pressed a lever, which brought a flat weight down upon the sheet, and one page was printed. Carefully lifting this first page from the form, the workman handed it to Sarah.

It was a small page, only eight by four and a half inches, with the tiny print in two columns. But it was with a feeling of pride and excitement such as she had never before known that Sarah held this small page, with the ink still wet upon it.

"I must take it to my desk and read it carefully," she said. "There must be no mistakes in this first issue of the *Ladies' Magazine.*"

A week later Sarah held in her hands the first completed magazine of fifty-two pages, all set by hand from hand-written manuscript and put together by hand. She studied it critically and found that, in spite of all her careful proof-reading, some errors had crept in. Almost involuntarily, her pen went to work, correcting these errors on the finished magazine.

John Putnam came in, waving his first copy with a jubilant air. "It is magnificent!" he declared. "You have produced a revolutionary book, Mrs. Hale!"

Sarah frowned. "There are still errors. I must have every copy brought to my desk so I can correct it."

The publisher stared at her in amazement. "That's impossible! A thousand copies! Why, Mrs. Hale, you must realize that no publication is entirely free from typographical errors!"

"Nevertheless I shall correct as many as I can," Sarah stated firmly. And so some of this first issue went forth with corrections in Sarah's own slanting script.

She was not as jubilant as was her publisher. She could see where the magazine had fallen short of what she hoped for. True, she had been able to express some of her dearest ideas. Having to write most of the material herself, she had spoken out for "infant schools" in one article. In another she had demanded "No Sex in Education," declaring that girls should receive an education equal to that of their brothers. Still another of her articles had urged that women be trained as teachers of young children. She had inaugurated a fictional series, which she called "Sketches of American Character."

But she did not want to *write* the magazine. She wanted to *edit* it. She hoped to be able to attract the best writers in the country as contributors. She realized that only by so doing could she make her magazine really contribute to the education of the women of the country. Therefore she had inserted a notice inviting American authors to send material. She would pay them well. If only they would respond!

She carried a copy of the magazine home to show the children. They were even more delighted than John Putnam had been. Young David's brown eyes, so like his father's, regarded his mother with pride and affection.

"It is the best magazine I have ever seen!" he declared. "Why, Mother, it is interesting enough for even men to read."

Sarah hugged him. "Coming from the man of my house, that is real praise. Would you really subscribe to it, sir?"

Smiling seriously, David answered, "Indeed I would, Mrs. Hale. Please let my name head your subscription list!"

6

ISSUES APLENTY

Involved as she was with the magazine, Sarah still managed to spend a good deal of time with her children. One of their favorite diversions was to take long walks through the historic city, while Sarah pointed out landmarks and related the stirring events that had taken place at each.

Born only twelve years after the signing of the Declaration of Independence, with a father who had been active in the War of Revolution, Sarah felt that she had "grown up" with the new nation. Every notable incident in its history was familiar to her. Love and pride in her country were an integral part of her nature, and she never missed an opportunity to instil the same love and pride in her children.

One bright, sunny afternoon soon after their arrival in Boston, they were taking one of these walks. Their destination was Breed's Hill, across the Charles River, where on June 17, 1775, American troops had met British soldiers in battle.

Down across Boston Commons they strolled, Sarah walking erect and proud among her chattering children. They did not pause to read the inscriptions on the stones in the little cemetery on the Boylston Street side. The children had already seen these and knew the stories of Gilbert Stuart, the painter, and of the other noted men buried there. Pointing, recalling the things they had learned, they passed King's Chapel and the Boston Public Latin School where Benjamin Franklin had received his early education. Past the old State House they paused briefly at the site of the Boston Massacre and looked with reverence at the circle marked in the middle of the street to show the spot where early patriots had shed their blood for their country.

It was a long walk, but the children were used to such rambles with their mother. Her stories made the time pass without notice. She began to tell them about the Bunker Hill Monument, which they were on their way to see.

"When General Lafayette was in this country four years ago, he came to Newport. Did you know that I met him and shook hands with him?"

The children goggled up at their mother. How wonderful it must have been to have spoken to and shaken hands with the great Frenchman.

"He came up here to Boston to lay the cornerstone of the monument to the heroes of the Battle of Bunker Hill. How I wish I'd been here then! Senator Daniel Webster gave the dedicatory address, and there was a great parade—more than two hundred soldiers who fought in the Revolution marched in it. Your Grandfather Buell could have marched in it if he had still been alive."

She paused, remembering her father. One of the things that had made it easier for her to leave Newport had been the fact that both parents had died. Except for the loyal Hannah, there was none of her immediate family left in the town.

The children were staring ahead, their eyes bright, each one eager to be the first to catch sight of the towering spire of the monument.

"Of course the monument isn't finished yet, but after four years—well, it should be far enough along to be worth seeing!" Sarah assured them.

Sarah slowed her footsteps as she neared Breed's Hill, where the small American army had thrown up its redoubts fifty-four years earlier. As her eyes scanned the hilltop, a feeling of shame made her cheeks burn. There on the crest, where she had expected to see a noble monolith, stood an ugly gray stone structure some forty feet high. Its jagged top edge showed that the work was unfinished. Although Sarah had not expected to see a completed monument, the desolation and confusion of the scene shocked her. No workmen were to be seen, and carelessly strewn about were tons of granite blocks, timbers—all the debris of a hastily abandoned job.

"What's the matter, Mother?" little Josepha asked. "Where's the monument?"

"There it is," David answered, pointing. "Mother said it wasn't finished yet. It will look different when it is."

"*When* it is?" Sarah's voice was a shocked whisper. "When will that be? Why, the work is abandoned! Look at the dirt and grime covering everything. Nothing is being done—nothing has been done for a long time! They have given it up! Oh, how could they?"

The children caught their mother's feeling of sadness. In silence they turned and made their way slowly homeward.

Sarah's shock soon turned into indignation. Sitting at her desk in the office of Putnam and Hunt, she picked up her pen, jabbed it furiously into the inkpot, and began to write.

As she wrote her wrath grew and her hand flew over the pages. Suddenly she stopped and stared at her words. As she reread them, her anger slowly cooled and her sense of caution took over.

"I won't accomplish anything by flying at their throats in this way," she murmured. "What I want is to get that monument finished. What I feel does not matter—I must not let it circumvent my purpose."

She crumpled up the pages she had written, pages aflame with indignation at the men who had started such a noble work and then dropped it, one-sixth done. She rose slowly from her desk and sought out Mr. Putnam, who had become her good friend. Putnam listened to Sarah's questions and then told her what had happened. The Monument Association was composed of patriotic and reliable men who had donated a great deal of their own money toward the project and had sought subscriptions from others. But already all the collected money had been spent, and sixteen thousand dollars more than that. The supporters of the idea had begged and pled for more money, but none had come in. They could not go on.

"Well then," Sarah said slowly, "I think I must make an appeal to our readers—to the women——"

"What good would that do?" Putnam asked. "They'd have to get the money from the men. And if the men have not contributed in their own names, it is not likely that they'll let their wives have money to donate."

"If the women went about it meekly, perhaps . . ."

"And what's more," the publisher went on, "magazines don't ask their readers to donate money to causes. It's difficult enough to get paid subscriptions. I don't think we could start something like that."

Sarah assumed her most gentle smile. "Why not, sir?" she asked quietly. "You have pioneered in publishing a woman's magazine. Why not lead the way in this as well?"

A twinkle came into Putnam's eyes. "You manage to get your own way every time, Mrs. Hale. Perhaps you are right again. Do whatever you think best."

"Thank you, sir." Then she added firmly, "But I do not intend to jump into this right now while my feelings are so stirred. I shall move slowly and carefully."

Yes, she thought as she returned to her desk, she would study the question; she would talk to Mr. Webster, to Dr. Warren who had purchased the land for the monument, and to others. She would let the public know of her interest and, if possible, undermine any opposition *before* she made her appeal for funds.

Sarah felt that she could do this because already she was becoming known in Boston. A stanch Episcopalian, she had immediately joined the congregation of St. Paul's Cathedral where Daniel Webster was a pew holder. Although St. Paul's had been built only eight years before, it numbered among its congregation some of the most influential men and women of the city. Sarah, with her quiet air of refinement, was cordially accepted, even though she held the unique position of "editress" of a woman's magazine.

She was already a noticeable figure at lectures and concerts attended by the intellectuals. But she was even better known in the poorer, shabbier areas of the city, for she was finding that here in Boston there were aspects of life of which she had been wholly unaware. The hospitals, overcrowded and poorly kept with their masses of suffering people, the workhouses, the dockside shanties, all emphasized the inequality between the rich and the poor—and between men and women too—which had been almost unknown in the pleasant farm communities of New Hampshire. Day after day Sarah's small, erect figure in its inconspicuous dark dress could be seen in the hovels of neglected families or on the cluttered, unkempt streets near the docks. So sincere was her interest, and so great her tact, that no offense was taken, and she was accepted by the poor and miserable as freely as by the rich and prosperous.

Slowly, surely an idea was burgeoning in her mind. She began to see that these people, particularly the women of these areas, needed an articulate champion. Someone must speak out boldly and unfalteringly to win for them some measure of self-respect and security.

Sometimes Sarah felt almost overwhelmed by the multitude of problems presented by the city, her work, and her family. But she never let panic seize her. Calmly, one by one, she dealt with each phase as promptly and adequately as she could. But the *Ladies' Magazine* was her chief concern.

One day Putnam found her seated at a table littered with the leading journals of the day, studying each one with frowning attention. He grinned affably.

"Are you finding anything in those men's magazines that you want to imitate?" he teased.

Sarah shook her head. "Nothing to imitate and much to avoid. This custom of 'borrowing' stories and articles from the English papers is one I do *not* care for. Borrowing!" She sniffed delicately. " 'Stealing' would be a better word, for no payment is ever made."

"Well," the publisher said, "you must admit that it's economical."

"But it isn't honest. And it's not even very clever, for these things are written to appeal to the British, not the American, reader. I am going to make it widely known that our magazine does not 'borrow' from the British and that we intend to pay American writers for American material."

"Another of your revolutionary ideas, Mrs. Hale. But I agree with you. Such a stand should attract more readers than ever."

"Not only readers, Mr. Putnam," Sarah pointed out, "but authors as well. When word gets around that the *Ladies' Magazine* is paying American authors and using only American material, we should get contributions that have a special interest for our readers. This British material has very little, if any, application to our way of life. And," she said with sudden energy, "there's another thing. I am going to try to get the authors to use their own names—not just their initials or a *nom de plume* the way they do so persistently."

The publisher frowned. "I don't know—" he began hesitantly.

"Oh," Sarah conceded, "I know that at times it is more convenient, and sometimes more tactful, to use a pen name. In the early issues of our magazine I've had to write so much of the material myself that I didn't dare sign my name to everything. The public would have thought it strange that we had no contributors at all! As editor, I do feel that it is sometimes best to hide my authorship. But these special considerations aside, I feel that it will help our subscription list to have the contributors sign their names."

Putnam was still unconvinced. Sarah picked up a letter from her desk.

"This letter came yesterday. In it the writer praises the article by Emma Willard, and asks that we publish more of Mrs. Willard's work. There have been other requests of the same sort. You see, sir, after only a few issues we have one author that our readers are demanding. The fact that they know her name, know that she is a bona fide person, has won their interest. In time we can build up the reputation of our best writers so that the public demands their work and will buy our magazine in order to obtain it."

Putnam scratched his chin thoughtfully. This was an entirely new viewpoint.

"Also, sir," Sarah persisted, "when an author signs his name it has the effect of vouching for the truth of what he writes. It shows, at any rate, that he is not afraid or ashamed of his views."

Putnam chuckled. "Right, as usual, Mrs. Hale. Go ahead with your plan. I'll stand back of anything you promise."

Sarah wasted no time gloating over this triumph. She had other problems to solve. She had instituted a department of "Household Helps," but she did not like that title for the column. She wanted something more dignified, more attractive, something that would permit women to have a feeling of pride in their work in the home. She scribbled down several words and phrases, trying them out: "Home Helps," "Home Science," "Household Science," and then suddenly a new phrase came to mind—"Domestic Science."

"That's it!" she said aloud. "Under this title the meanest household chore becomes a dignified occupation. Domestic Science!" With a flourish she wrote it at the top of the large sheet of foolscap on which she composed her articles and editorials, smiling as she wrote. She knew her readers would like it.

One series of articles by Sarah was causing a great deal of comment in the homes and in the press. In preparing them, Sarah was grateful for the anonymity afforded by the custom of not signing articles. These articles were headed "Confessions of a Husband," and were being used to promote Sarah's favorite theme: the higher education of women. Each month a letter from the supposed husband set forth in glowing terms the advantages he enjoyed because he had had the good sense to marry an educated woman. He could talk to her as to an equal; she could entertain his friends with commendable skill; she could direct the children in their education and their behavior. But best of all, her education made her aware of true values, and as a result she was thrifty and wise in the management of the home.

Sometimes, as a foil to the happy husband's situation, Sarah would write an article showing the other side of the picture. A husband married to an uneducated girl having all sorts of difficulties due to his wife's ignorance and her inability to understand him and his problems.

The "Confessions of a Husband" were discussed at sewing circles, over teacups, and in drawing rooms, the arguments sometimes growing heated and sharp. Even newspapers took up the debate, some poking fun at the delusions of a man who obviously was trying to hold onto his place as head of the home, while a domineering, so-called "educated" wife was slowly but surely crowding him out.

Sarah was delighted at the furor her articles were causing, especially among rival journals. As editors from New York to Maine took up the gauntlet and either supported or made fun of the "husband's" theories, the spotlight of attention was focused on the *Ladies' Magazine,* and the circulation grew apace.

Involved though she was with her editorial duties, Sarah kept her after-office hours free for her children. They always had supper together, and afterward Sarah would listen to their lessons and their accounts of the day's activities. Then came reading aloud, singing, and prayers before the children were tucked into bed.

This was the role Sarah loved best. She enjoyed her editorial work and handled it with businesslike, unsentimental efficiency. But with her children she was tender and affectionate, teaching them by her own example serenity and gentleness. From little incidents she drew lessons which she brought home to the children through rhymes and stories and games. She held their father up to them as a shining example —a man who was the very epitome of kindness, industry, and intelligence.

Sarah was proud of her children and watched their physical growth with satisfaction. David, his mother's stand-by and companion, was very much like his father—tall, slenderly built, brown-eyed. At fourteen, he was truly the "man of the family." But Horatio was not far behind his brother. From babyhood he had shown a tremendous interest in words and language, and was now reading German and French with facility. Even William, nearing seven, was reading books designed for much older children, while the two little girls easily kept pace with their brothers. They were beautiful and intelligent children, skilled in the social graces and far advanced in their education.

Sarah became especially conscious of all this when, in the fall of 1829, the first break came in the little family. It was not really a sad break, and Sarah could not help but feel a glow of pride when young David was accepted as a cadet at West Point. It was not only his Grandfather Buell's service in the War of Rebellion that obtained this appointment. Though he was only fourteen, his scholarship was so outstanding that he had no difficulty with the preliminary tests and Sarah had to acknowledge that her training and instruction had helped her son achieve this honor. But her pride in David was mingled with sorrow at seeing him leave the little family circle she had held intact with so much effort. She was determined, however, not to mar his triumph. Her clear hazel eyes regarded him fondly but without tears as she bade him good-by.

"Write often, David. Let us share your new life and friends and experiences."

"Of course, Mother," David promised.

His brothers and sisters crowded around him as he climbed into the stagecoach that would carry him to Albany, where he would take passage on a riverboat for West Point. But Sarah stood back, the better to see this handsome young son as he waved farewell from the coach steps.

After David had gone, Sarah tried to fill the gap he left by more and more work. Her employers also published a little bimonthly magazine for children called the *Juvenile Miscellany.* Like the *Ladies' Magazine,* it was a pioneer in its field and Sarah, who was delighted with the idea of a special magazine for children, contributed many little poems to it. Some of these she had composed for the pleasure of her own youngsters, and among these was little Josepha's favorite. It was a set of verses that told the story of Mary Tucker and her lamb at Sarah's first school.

After Horatio entered Harvard College, Sarah needed frequent sums of money for her two oldest sons, so she decided to put her verses into a small book for children. She asked her daughters to help her decide which poems to include.

" 'Mary Had a Little Lamb,' " Josepha declared without hesitation, and began to recite the words.

Sarah smiled. "That has always been your favorite, hasn't it, Josepha?"

"Yes. And I like the story about how the examination was interrupted. Why didn't you put that part into the poem, Mother?"

"That would make it too long, I'm afraid. What poem do you suggest, Frances?"

"Oh, 'It Snows!' I like that:

> *"'It snows!' cried the schoolboy,*
> *'Hurrah!' and his shout*
> *Is ringing through parlor and hall,*
> *While swift as the wing of a swallow, he's out,*
> *And his playmates have answered his call . . . "*

" 'Birds! Birds!' " William interrupted his sister's recitation. "Mother wrote that 'specially for me." And he began:

> *"If ever I see*
> *On bush or tree,*
> *Young birds in a pretty nest,*
> *I must not in my play*
> *Steal the birds away,*
> *To grieve their mother's breast."*

Sarah drew the boy close. How well she remembered composing those lines for William. He had come home with an excited tale about some small friends who had robbed a bird's nest, and she had, on the spur of the moment, answered him with the rhyme.

One by one they named their favorites, and Sarah put them all in her new book, *Poems for Our Children* (1830). As with her other books, this one, published by Marsh, Capen and Lyon, proved an immediate success. One day Dr. Lowell Mason, the foremost musician and composer of Boston, came to her office carrying a copy of the small, blue-backed book.

"Mrs. Hale," the composer began, "I would like to set some of your verses to music. I have long believed that children learn most quickly through music and rhythm. I hope to be able to convince the schools that they should teach singing. At present there is nothing for them to use for this purpose. But your verses and my music would provide the needed material. May I do this?"

Sarah's eyes glowed. "Why, of course, Dr. Mason! That's the way I've taught my children many things. I sing little rhymes to them, they learn them easily, and the lessons become a part of them—unrecognized, perhaps, but powerful."

"There are only fifteen poems in your book, some of which are not quite suitable for my purpose. Would you consider writing some others? In your introduction you promised the children that you would do so."

"I'll do my best," Sarah promised, "though my children are growing past the age when they are pleased with simple little rhymes. But I would be happy to contribute to such a worthwhile new project."

The composer took Sarah's small hand into his. He looked down into her eyes and said gently, "You are doing a great service for womankind, Mrs. Hale. I am sure you will serve the children also."

This new venture, along with all of Sarah's other activities, required a great deal of time. After the verses were edited to Dr. Mason's approval, the music had to be composed and the printing done. Thus it was not until 1831 that schoolchildren of Boston were given *The Juvenile Lyre* and were permitted to sing in their classrooms.

Sarah felt an inner glow of pride that she had played a part in this innovation in public schools. Often of an evening she would sit with her children and sing the songs as Dr. Mason had meant them to be sung. The little program always included Josepha's favorite.

7

A BOLD CHALLENGE

JOHN PUTNAM CAME INTO SARAH'S OFFICE CARRYING A
sheaf of papers. He was beaming.

"My lady editress is certainly stirring things up!" he
said, smiling down at Sarah. "The sincerest flattery, you
know, is imitation. And we are being imitated—if you can
call it that!"

He laid a magazine on Sarah's desk. "A fellow down in
Philadelphia named Godey has started to publish a *'Lady's
Book.'* This is his first issue."

Sarah picked up the small journal, dated July, 1830, and
scanned it curiously. "Why, it's not even a good imitation of
our magazine!" she said curtly. "It is just a jumble of stories
and articles from English magazines—stolen, too, no doubt."

Pirating of British material always annoyed her. She had
refused to adopt this practice, though it was followed by
publishers throughout the country.

"That's right," Putnam agreed. "I tell you, Mrs. Hale, the
thing that's making our *Ladies' Magazine* so noteworthy is
the way you go at things. You are not afraid to attack bad

71

practices—whether in the publishing field or in society. And your editorials are really getting attention. Read this!"

He placed a New York City newspaper before her. An item was circled in red ink. Sarah read it and her pale, oval face flushed with pleasure. The item was by a leading editor and it highly praised the "foresight of the lady editress on the editorials she has been writing since March, pleading with the women of the country to donate funds to make possible the completion of the Bunker Hill Monument."

Sarah sighed as she finished. "We are not getting ahead very fast with that campaign. Oh, a few dollars are coming in, but not nearly enough."

Putnam laid another paper on her desk. "Maybe this is one reason."

As Sarah scanned the marked article, her look of pleasure changed to one of annoyance. This Boston editor had not agreed with the New York editor. She read:

> The Lady Editress asks her female readers to subscribe funds for the completion of the Bunker Hill Monument. Now, we agree with the fair editress that the monument should be completed, but we do not agree with her wisdom in calling on women to contribute. Where, we should like to ask the editress, are the women to obtain this money? From their natural benefactors, of course, and only from them. And since the men have already indicated that they do not have the needful funds, how on earth are their wives and daughters going to subscribe to the passionate plea of our fair competitor?

"It's always the same story!" Sarah cried. "Women have nothing, nothing of their own! Even those poor women who take in washing for the sailors cannot keep for themselves and their children the few pennies they earn by their back-breaking work. But he is right. The women can't contribute very much, as I have learned."

"These other notices are about equally divided," the publisher went on. "Some praise your courage and tact; others complain that you are invading man's domain. The more sagacious editors realize that your demands for the employment of women teachers, for the abolishment of corporal punishment in the schools, and for the establishment of infant schools are all sound. Others——" He shrugged. "Well, your 'Confessions of a Husband' seem to irk them greatly."

Sarah said meditatively, "I have to smile when I recall how afraid I was at first that I could never find enough material to fill the magazine, for issue after issue. Now my greatest problem is to decide what to select and what to emphasize."

"Well, you have shown an amazing skill at selecting the things that make people sit up and take notice. You have blazed a number of journalistic trails through our *Ladies' Magazine*, and I am mighty proud to be the publisher responsible!"

He laid the sheaf of papers and magazines on her desk and left. After glancing at two or three, Sarah laid them aside. She had work to do. She did not intend to abandon her campaign for funds with which to complete the Bunker Hill Monument. After months of careful study, she had begun her active campaign through editorials during the past spring. And she would continue until she was sure there was nothing further to be gained.

Perhaps right now it would be wise to smoothe the ruffled feathers of the angry Boston men. She could write a placating editorial, assuring them that women did not intend to invade their domain, that they merely intended to lend a feeble helping hand. What if she listed some of the prominent women who had consented to act on her central committee

for collecting the funds—her Committee of Correspondence?
When the annoyed gentlemen realized that some of the most
influential men of the city were permitting their wives to act
in this campaign, they would think again before objecting.

A canny smile curved her lips as she dipped her pen into
the inkpot and began to write. After a few tactful comments
meant to appease the indignant editors, she suggested that
women aim at contributing only one dollar, which they could
obtain by industry, economy, or self-denial. She concluded:
"This appeal is subscribed to by the Committee of Correspondence, comprising Mrs. Caleb Loring, Mrs. John
Pierpont, Mrs. A. H. Everett, Mrs. Nathan Hale . . ." and
so on down through the list of women whose names were
known throughout New England.

When she had finished she paused. Even this was not
enough . . . She needed something emotional—a poem.
Scribbling furiously, crossing out a word here and there,
pausing for the right adjective or verb, she wrote the poem
with which to clinch her appeal. "The Last of the Band"
indicated the thoughts of the last survivor of the Battle of
Bunker Hill when he knew that his countrymen would not
contribute a mite to a monument that would preserve for
posterity the honor of their heroic battle. After telling how he
saw the monument begun, and how he had hoped to see it
finished before he died, the old soldier cried:

> "I have no thirst for glory—none—
>   We never bartered blood for fame;
> But 'twas the thought, when we were gone,
>   Our children had preserved the name
> On a proud record, fair to show,
> Where men—not soldiers—met the foe.
>
> "They're gone—those old men all are gone!
>   Like autumn's latest leaves they passed.

> Last of the Band, I am alone,
>   Quivering in age's wintry blast.
> But ere I mingle with the dust
> Shall I not see my Country just?"

Sarah found that her judgment had again been right. The poem was recited everywhere, and a small flood of dollars swamped her desk. But still not enough. When the contributions ceased, the total amount sent in by women was found to be less than three thousand dollars. But Sarah was not wholly discouraged. The men had done little better, and it was decided to abandon the monument for a time.

Though busy with the Monument Fund campaign, Sarah found time to consider her daughters' education. The autumn of 1830 was approaching and the girls' school must be selected. If only there were a higher school for girls in Boston. But there wasn't. And though Frances Ann was only eleven and Josepha was not yet ten, both girls were so advanced that the little instruction available to girls held no challenge for their keen, inquisitive minds. Sarah's method of teaching through happy activity had supplemented their scant formal schooling, which was, for girls, sketchy at best. But they were ready now for advanced study, which their mother did not have time or, she felt, preparation, to give them.

It seemed to Sarah that there was but one solution to the problem. The girls would have to be sent away to school. There were a few "female seminaries" that provided a higher education for women, but even in these advanced schools the courses hardly equaled those taught at schools for young men. Nevertheless they were a step in the right direction—the direction in which Sarah had been pointing ever since she undertook to teach her first school at Newport.

The most fashionable female seminary for young ladies

from the Boston area was one in which Sarah was greatly interested. It had been established by one of her own former teachers, Miss Catherine Fiske, at Keene, New Hampshire. It was not far from Sarah's old home, and she felt that it would be good for the girls to return to the country district she had loved. She could now afford to send her daughters to any school they chose, and she was glad that she was able to provide for them as their father would have done. She shrank from being separated from them, but it was best for them and she decided to let them go.

"You must have new dresses and bonnets and cloaks," Sarah said, looking fondly at the two pretty girls. "We'll have Mrs. Winters in to make them. Oh, how I wish your Aunt Hannah were here to help!"

Mrs. Winters was notified and arrived a few days later with her arms full of French magazines.

"I brought these so the little ladies could pick out the newest styles. They'll want to be right in fashion, no doubt," the dressmaker said, spreading the magazines before the girls' delighted eyes.

Sarah picked one up, fluttered the pages through her fingers, and could not repress a slight shudder.

"These are horrible!" she exclaimed. "No, my girls want pretty dresses, but nothing like these. Look at them, Mrs. Winters—rows and rows of soutache and braid, tucks and ruffles. Bows scattered here and there. They are positively ugly! I've purchased fine materials for their dresses and I don't want them spoiled. I want them to look like young girls—not like Paris ladies!"

Mrs. Winters was vexed. She let her eyes go over Sarah's own simple dark dress. Then she said, "Well, many a Boston lady is having me copy these pictures exactly. And I thought, since you are the editress of a ladies' magazine, you'd naturally want your daughters to be in high style."

"High style doesn't interest me in the least," Sarah answered. "I have purposely kept women's fashions out of the *Ladies' Magazine* and have constantly told my readers to wear the style that suits their personality—but to realize that simplicity is the height of elegance."

The dressmaker sniffed. "Well, ma'am, each to his taste, say I. You show me how you want the misses' dresses made and I'll make them."

The next few weeks were busy ones as two neat wardrobes were prepared. But finally all was done, and the two little girls, feeling very grown-up in their ankle-length dresses and feather-trimmed bonnets, kissed their mother good-by and settled themselves in the stagecoach for the long journey to Keene.

Sarah's encounter with the dressmaker was echoed soon after the girls had left. The publisher of the *Ladies' Magazine* had often suggested to Sarah that she use fashion plates, as so many journals were beginning to do, but Sarah did not like the suggestion.

"The only pictures we can obtain are of French styles," she pointed out. "I hardly think they are suitable for American women. They're ugly, with all those frills and furbelows. Oh Mr. Putnam, let's not descend to offering such styles to our readers. If we could get some American fashions . . ."

John Putnam laughed. "Little chance of that, I fear. Why, even if an American artist wanted to draw style plates, he'd have to copy the French. There's no such thing as an American fashion."

"Well then, let's avoid the whole matter."

For more than two years Sarah had withstood the demand

for fashion plates in the *Ladies' Magazine*, but she could hold off no longer when Mr. Putnam brought an engraving and laid it on her desk.

"We are going to start using fashion plates," he said without preamble. "This is the first one."

Sarah stared in horror at the picture and then, unable to stop, broke into unexpected laughter.

"Oh sir!" she managed to say at last. "Can you imagine any woman going about attired like that?"

"I'll admit that I can't imagine you in that dress, Mrs. Hale. But I am sure my wife would be delighted to have one. In fact," he added with a twinkle in his eye, "it is she who insists that we publish fashions, and she picked this one for the first."

Sarah forced herself to look again at the engraving. It showed a gown so low-cut that it was almost falling off the shoulders of the wearer; the sleeves were two enormous puffs, and the skirt was trimmed with two wide rows of elaborate lace and embroidery. The outfit was topped by a hat of enormous size and intricate design, under which only two crinkly puffs of hair could be seen. But in order that the hair style be made clear, separate pictures showed both front and back of the head with the hat removed.

Sarah shook her head slowly. "I know of no Boston woman who could copy that hairdress—or would want to. It must be excruciating—those twists and knobs and—and —flummididdles!" she added crossly.

But Sarah knew she had lost this battle. After all, the publisher was boss, and, though he gave her an almost entirely free hand, if his wife wanted fashion plates, fashion plates they must have. However, Sarah promised herself that she would not meekly submit. She was unaccustomed to displaying irritation, but she did not hide her feeling as she wrote her editorial on the new department:

"There is no part of our duty as editor of a ladies' journal which we feel so reluctant to perform as to promote extravagance in women's clothing by exhibiting the fashions of dress. The result of the finest toilet should be an elegant woman, not an elegantly dressed woman." She went on to declare that it ill became American women to copy every frippery and ornament invented by French dressmakers and English milliners.

So far, in more than two years as editor, Sarah had lost few debates concerning the magazine's policy, which is perhaps why she felt this defeat so keenly. Then she took courage again: she would do what she could to choose the simplest, most dignified fashions available. Let the women have their fashion plates, but let her good taste direct them, gently but firmly, toward the best in whatever fashion was prevailing. She would act as the rein to curb her readers' exuberance in style and extravagance in expenditure.

"Why cannot American women find a simple and becoming mode that could be retained for centuries, thus saving all the energy, concern, and expense of keeping in style?" she asked reasonably.

She knew this was an impossible suggestion, and, half poking fun at her own idea, she related: "At one time it was customary for ladies and gentlemen to wear shoes with toes a foot and a half long, and turned up like sleigh runners. The clergy preached a crusade against these ornaments without effect. Hence we may learn that whatever may be said against fashion, it is useless to decry it. We are still rocked in fashionable cradles and buried in fashionable coffins!"

Now, with only William at home, Sarah felt desperately

alone. Horatio had chosen to board at Harvard, so that he would have more time to study, with the needed books at hand in the college library. He came home only on week ends. Sarah spent more and more time with her little boy. And William responded with such an enthusiasm and an affectionate heart that the companionship was the happiest part of Sarah's winter.

Since Sarah now had a little more freedom from family responsibilities, she threw herself wholeheartedly into the study of the condition of the women of Boston, particularly the wives of seamen. She had long been aware of the problems facing the families of these men—the backbone of Boston's prosperity. For Boston lived from the sea. Her ships encircled the globe, and all over the world Americans were known as Boston Men. The voyages were long; the men who manned the ships would be away from home for months at a time—sometimes for a year or two. While they were gone, their families must exist as best they could. There was scarcely any work that a woman could do to eke out a living, and the husband left her scanty funds when he set out on his dangerous journey, from which, indeed, he might never return.

Sarah was appalled at the poverty, the dirt and hunger she found throughout Shanty Town, where the seamen's families lived. Sarah herself had been poor—but it was not poverty like this. She had had a good home, warm clothing, plenty of nourishing food, and plenty of books. These families had none of these things.

"I don't believe the families on Beacon Street or Louisburg Square have any idea what exists on the waterfront," she mused. "I shall tell them." And she did. She wrote of the deprivations and hopelessness of the women whose husbands could command no more than from ten to eighteen dollars a month. After presenting the problem, she offered a solution: the formation of a society to assist these families.

By now Sarah's editorials had become so influential that they were actually shaping the thought and action of the women of Boston and of neighboring New England cities. The suggestion that a woman's society be organized was eagerly seized upon by Sarah's readers. It was a new, daring idea. Women had never before, in this country, organized for such a purpose. At church, on the street, in the shops, women gathered in small knots and talked it over.

"Why not?" the more courageous asked. "Why can't women form an organization? Men do! Why, that's the very first thing they do when they want to accomplish anything. Remember the Bunker Hill Monument Association? All men! And the Massachusetts Historical Association? Men, again. I tell you, Mrs. Hale is right. Women can join forces if they only have the gumption."

The first meeting was held in Faneuil Hall in the spring of 1833. Sarah came dressed in her customary dark silk, with a touch of snowy lace at throat and wrists. Her chestnut hair fell in soft curls below a lace cap, framing her pale oval face. It was an old-fashioned costume and hair style, but it was the way David had known and loved her and Sarah would not change. She wore the outmoded attire with such elegance and dignity that no one thought to criticize it.

The hall was filled as Sarah, standing before the eager, curious women, outlined her project:

"The only means of adding to their pitiful income is by hard work—either going into domestic service in some family or taking washing into their homes—or, if they are skilled, by doing dressmaking. This last is, of course, the easiest and the most satisfactory method, even though it is difficult work. My idea is to provide some sort of needlework for the mothers of families, for older girls, and for wives who must add to their meager funds or starve."

She looked out over her attentive audience. "Perhaps I should tell you ladies," she went on gently, "something about the actual situation in these families. Or perhaps, when our organization is complete, you will take the time, one day, to visit Boston's well-named Shanty Town and see for yourselves the conditions there."

The listeners, well-dressed, well-fed, and well-intentioned women, nodded. They really wanted to see, now that their attention had been directed to the problem.

Sarah went on: "The slop shops—also well named—are miserable establishments that exist only for the profit of the owner. They pay a woman six cents for making a shirt or a pair of trousers. The most experienced needlewoman, sewing as fast as her fingers can fly, working from daylight to dark, cannot earn more than from sixty cents to one dollar a week. With this pittance she must feed and clothe her family, buy fuel and light, and pay rent. That same shirt for which she was paid six cents to make, and in which is fifteen cents' worth of material—a total cost to the shop owner of twenty-one cents, sells to the seaman—perhaps to the woman's own husband—for one dollar!

"I have studied on this, and I know that we could pay the needlewoman more than the slop shop pays her; and we can sell the garment to the seamen for less than the slop shop charges—and we can still make a profit."

A murmur of remonstrance rose. A woman stood up: "Madame President——"

Sarah smiled and shook her head. "We have no organization as yet, no officers. I am simply a Boston woman interested in improving a shameful situation."

"Well, anyway, Mrs. Hale, why don't we sell for the same price as the slop shops? If we have extra money, extra profit, we can use it to purchase food and clothes for the families. I am quite sure that we could show better judgment in spending this money than those uneducated, untrained women could."

Sarah concealed the repugnance she felt at the suggested idea by smiling graciously and replying gently: "That is one way of handling the situation. But it does have one drawback. How will those women ever learn to handle money if they are never given the opportunity to try? And I feel quite sure that it is better to let the women earn, and receive, money than it is to give them anything. I feel that we can build up self-respect and independence only through giving the needy adequate work with fair pay."

This was a new idea to the women. Up to this point, their charitable work had consisted in handing out food and clothing—not work or money for work done. They began to chatter about it. Sarah let them talk until one woman stood up to speak. Only then did Sarah rap for order.

"Mrs. Hale," the woman began, "aren't you afraid? Have you realized that the slop-shop owners are not going to like this invasion of their business—undercutting their prices. There may be trouble, real trouble . . ."

Consternation appeared on other faces. That was true: there was no telling what the slop-shop owners might do. They were probably disreputable men who feared no one and would stop at nothing. Anxious eyes turned to Sarah.

She stood there, small and confident, erect and poised. "Yes, ladies," she admitted quietly, "it is dangerous. It is a bold challenge. But if we stand united, we can override any threat, any danger . . ."

Her confidence won. The Boston Seaman's Friend Society was organized and Sarah was then and there elected its first president.

Sitting in her office next day, writing the editorial that would tell the world what these Boston women had dared to undertake, Sarah's eyes grew dreamy.

"We'll need a store from which to sell the garments the women make," she mused. "Later we'll open an industrial training school for girls and a day nursery where the working mothers can leave their children to be cared for and taught. And a library—a free library—to provide the books they've never had. Maybe we can provide books not only for the women but for the seamen too. How wonderful that would be. Perhaps, someday, such a library in every large seaport . . ."

She looked up to see her new employer standing in front of her desk. It was Mr. Marsh of the firm of Marsh, Capen, and Lyon, which had recently purchased the *Ladies' Magazine* from Putnam and Hunt.

"You're going to have a real fight on your hands, Mrs. Hale," he said slowly. "And not only from the slop-shop owners. Are you aware that the waterfront boardinghouses always get a percentage of the profits on the clothing sold to the men living there? These boardinghouse owners will be after you too."

"Perhaps," Sarah said serenely. "Perhaps we shall have to open our own boardinghouses. Trust me, Mr. Marsh—if we do, our houses will be clean and vermin-free, our food good and wholesome . . ." A sudden smile broke across her face. "That's a wonderful idea you have given me, Mr. Marsh. I trust it won't be long before you see it blossom."

Marsh shrugged helplessly, then he grinned. "John Putnam was right. Your mind is like a steel trap—ready to catch and hold any new idea. But don't give me credit, Mrs. Hale. The idea was yours, not mine."

Sarah smiled demurely. "Let's say it was the magazine's," she said.

8

A PRINCE INTERFERES

IN THE SPRING OF 1833 SARAH TOOK THE FIRST VACATION she had had in five years. She went to West Point to attend David's graduation. As she sat among other parents, watching the uniformed young men, their brass buttons gleaming, tears of pride and love filled her eyes. If only his father could be here too! she thought sadly. For David, recently turned eighteen, was the youngest in the class of a hundred and fifty, and yet he was graduating with high honors, only eighth from the top of the class.

All through the long commencement exercises that morning she was thinking how sad it was that the strange classmate of David's was not present with the others. She had been deeply interested in the "mad poet" David had written about during his first year. She had read the verses David had sent, begging her to buy them if she possibly could, because the author, Cadet Edgar Poe, was in desperate need of money. "His people send him nothing," David had written, "and he has traded his last blanket, even his candles, for things he needs or wants."

Sarah had found the poems strangely beautiful, but so

exotic and lyrical that they would have startled and confused
her readers. *Ladies' Magazine* was meeting enough opposition without introducing any such new poems, which appealed more to the emotions than to the moral sense. She
had returned the verses, with a kind note to the author,
feeling grieved and somehow just a bit responsible when
David had written that this eccentric young man had been
dismissed from the Academy after a court-martial, for gross
neglect of his duties.

David was commissioned a second lieutenant in the First
Artillery. After a brief vacation he was to report to his unit
at Beaufort, South Carolina.

Sarah's pride in her tall, handsome young son was tinged
with apprehension. Being alert to the historic and social
movements of her country, she knew that the chief duty of
the American army lay in handling and subduing hostile
Indian tribes. Only the year before, Black Hawk had been
defeated. Sarah had read many an account of this stubborn
war chief of the Sac and Fox tribes, and of his barbaric methods of fighting. Those tribes were quiet now, but in Georgia
the Cherokees were rebellious over their treatment by that
state. There might be real trouble there. And there were
other danger spots. Would David, a mere boy, even though
he was a second lieutenant, be sent against wily and un-
scrupulous Indians?

Sarah would not voice her anxiety, but she found it was
justified when, the following year, David wrote that his unit
had been ordered to Florida to help subdue the turbulent
Seminoles under their wild chief, Osceola. Now Sarah's
concern found only two sources of comfort—prayer and work.
Her prayers were silent, hidden deep in her heart. Her work,
the world could see and take note of.

In this year, 1834, the *Ladies' Magazine* had again

changed ownership, the famous lady editress going along
with the journal. James B. Dow, latest owner of the publication, moved its offices from the old address to new and more
spacious quarters at 362 Washington Street. At Sarah's suggestion the word "American" had been added to the title.
American Ladies' Magazine boasted material only by American authors and artists, written and drawn for its own special
readers.

The fashion plates still dimmed Sarah's satisfaction with
the journal. Though they had become one of the most
popular features, Sarah bitterly disliked the ruchings and
ruffles that so pleased her readers. She had tried, with little
success, to get the engravers to "Americanize" the styles; she
had written editorials against extravagance and over-orna-
mentation; she had even paid higher prices than competitors
for the fashion plates she used. Still, they did not please her
good taste and good sense.

Her family was scattered, with David fighting Indians in
Florida; Frances and Josepha now at Mrs. Emma Willard's
Female Seminary in Troy, New York; Horatio at Harvard,
and only William at home. Sarah was proud of her daughters'
acceptance at this already noted school. Young as they were,
the two girls had completed the work at Miss Fiske's seminary, and with flying colors had passed the entrance examina-
tions for the higher school. Again Sarah had proof that her
methods of instruction were valid.

But there was a still deeper satisfaction in having Frances
Ann and Sarah Josepha at Mrs. Willard's academy. Sarah
had played no small part in the success of this woman, who
had become one of her most cherished friends. She had
written many editorials praising the educator's aims and
methods. Each time Mrs. Willard had added a new study to
the curriculum for young ladies—mathematics, logic, phi-

losophy—the fact had been heralded in the *Ladies' Magazine*.

It was largely due to Sarah's articles that the school was such a success that Governor De Witt Clinton had finally persuaded the New York State Legislature to give "female seminaries" a share of the state's literary fund. This was the first time a state body had contributed a penny toward girls' education, and Sarah hailed the event as a triumph in the battle she had instigated for the right of women to a higher education.

Emma Willard's struggle to win recognition of the need for female academies was only one of the educational projects that Sarah assisted through the *Ladies' Magazine*. When Elizabeth Peabody was chosen by Bronson Alcott to assist him in the experimental school he opened in the Masonic Temple in Boston, Sarah gave a full account of the new venture. When Miss Peabody later introduced Friedrich Frobel's kindergarten plan to American children, Sarah praised the advanced teaching method. She herself had unwittingly employed many of the great German educator's ideas in her own parlor school for William, but she did not hesitate to join in the chorus that hailed Miss Peabody as the "mother of the kindergarten in America."

Any woman who was working for the advancement of women was assured of a prominent place in the magazine. It encouraged Mary Lyon, who was advocating that an institution be erected "designed exclusively for older young ladies preparing to teach, and soon to go forth to exert an influence in a variety of ways on the cause of education and religion." A teacher in various New Hampshire and Massachusetts schools, Miss Lyon was appalled at the lack of formal preparation given to the instructors of the nation's children. Like Sarah, she believed firmly that women made the best teachers of young children, and though, as yet, she had obtained no financial support from any individual or society, she still clung to her idea and urged its adoption.

And there was Catharine Esther Beecher, daughter of the Reverend Lyman Beecher, who in 1824 had opened a female seminary at Hartford, Connecticut, where she was assisted in teaching by her younger sister, Harriet. Miss Beecher won Sarah's lasting friendship and admiration through her elaborate plan to educate all the children in the country. Sarah could heartily endorse Miss Beecher's ambition, "The grand aim of this plan is to unite American women in an effort to provide a *Christian Education* for two million children in our country who are destitute of schools."

Now Sarah no longer had to write the largest part of the magazine. Authors flooded her desk with contributions. Women, particularly, knew that their work would be given preference over that of men, and hastened to express themselves in prose and verse. Sarah's readers loved the sweetly sentimental verses of Lydia Sigourney, Elizabeth Ellet, Emma Embury, and Caroline Gilman. Though most of her women contributors hesitated to sign their names to their work, gradually Sarah won them over to her way of thinking. When their signed contributions resulted in a definite following, they no longer objected to the new system.

Sarah did not confine her friendships to women, and among the men with whom she became acquainted was Dr. Oliver Wendell Holmes, who came one day to board at the house where Sarah took her meals. The twenty-five-year-old physician had already had two small books published—*The Harbinger: A May Gift*, in 1833, and a small volume of poems in 1836, shortly before he met Sarah.

He was diffident and whimsical about his work, and eagerly sought the advice and opinion of the lady editress, who had become a recognized authority in the journalistic world. Sarah had modestly accepted her position as one of the most popular writers of the day. Her first novel, *Northwood*, was still selling widely both in America and Europe. Her *Poems for Our Children*, was the best-known juvenile book in New England; and a little volume, *Flora's Interpreter*, dealing with the "language of flowers" was being republished year after year to meet the demand.

Now, in her scanty spare time, she was working on a book of essays developed from her popular series, "Sketches of American Character." Her interest in poetry and in essays was a bond between her and Dr. Holmes, and together they discussed their work. And, though Sarah was older and more experienced and better known, still she found that she could learn much from the younger writer. It was largely due to his forthright approach to life that Sarah abandoned some of the gentle tactics she had used to win readers and subscribers. She began to speak more freely and, at times, even caustically, of things that irritated her. Her observations as editor were reported with a frankness and a keenness of insight that she would not have dared use earlier. So, when her book, *Traits of American Life*, was finally published, it caused a small furor in the country.

In addition to their writing, Sarah and Dr. Holmes found other areas in which both had a deep interest. They discussed the need for women physicians and the unsanitary condition of the city's hospitals. Through the young physician's influence, Sarah was permitted to visit the hospitals and watch the doctors at work, and this intimate contact convinced her that she was right: women must be admitted to the practice of medicine.

All this time the Seaman's Friend Society, renamed the "Seaman's Aid Society," was expanding by leaps and bounds. By 1836 Sarah decided it was time to open the boardinghouse she had thought about years before. She placed her problem before the sympathetic young doctor.

"A few years ago," she told him, "I had an idea that some-day someone should open a boardinghouse for seamen—a place that would be clean and wholesome and run for the benefit of the men rather than to make a profit for un-scrupulous owners. The time seems ripe now to put this idea into effect, and it looks as if the task is left to me. No one else has shown any willingness to undertake the project. Will you help me, Dr. Holmes?"

The physician's lips formed a smile. "It will be a pleasure and an honor, Mrs. Hale."

Together they made many trips to the waterfront, looking for a vacant building. There were plenty of them, but most were filthy, vermin-ridden, and dilapidated. True, they were comparable to the buildings being used for seamen's board-inghouses, but Sarah wanted something much better. Fur-thermore, it would cost too much to clean and paint and renovate one.

Though Sarah had tried to keep her project a secret until she had obtained the structure she wanted, rumors had leaked out. The owners of any property that attracted Sarah began to ask questions, and when her purpose was suspected, they refused to sell or rent to her. One fellow was brutally frank:

"We ain't aimin' to run no competition to the houses already agoin'. Wouldn't be wise, I can tell ye that, ma'am."

Dr. Holmes sighed as they turned away. "I'm afraid you aren't very wise, Mrs. Hale. But neither am I!" His eyes twinkled.

Sarah nodded. "Mr. Putnam warned me long ago that it would be dangerous to try to compete with the filthy hovels we dignify with the term 'boardinghouse.' But I'm not worried—if only we can find a place to begin."

At last their search was rewarded: a sturdy, large building was found. Sarah's women helpers cleaned and painted and repaired the structure and brought furniture from their attics and porches.

Gently persistent, Sarah overcame every difficulty one by one, and finally the first Mariners' House was opened—a clean, good-looking building standing proudly among the ramshackle hovels of Shanty Town. At the opening ceremony Sarah, still president of the Society, was called upon to speak. Hazel eyes glowing with enthusiasm, she told the assembly:

"This is only the beginning. Someday we'll see in every port, clean, well-managed homes for seamen. These men deserve far better than they have yet received in the filthy boardinghouses that have charged exorbitant fees for the scantiest and poorest food and accommodations."

During this same year Sarah sponsored the opening of an industrial trade school for girls, where the daughters of the absent seamen could be taught sewing and other crafts by which they could earn enough to provide a fairly decent living. And no sooner was this school working smoothly than she started a day nursery so that the working mothers would have a suitable place to leave their young children while they were busy.

Sarah felt that there was no end to the things that should be done for these hitherto-neglected families. She spent many hours devising new projects. One of her dearest wishes was to give these people the opportunity to extend their limited horizons through reading, and in the summer of 1836 she established a free lending library. At first the library invited only girls and women to use its facilities, but before long it was opened to the men of the district. A branch was opened in the now-thriving Mariners' House, which Sarah hoped would be the beginning of a nation-wide series of mariners' libraries.

All these activities were making Sarah one of the best-known women in the country. Her desk was daily piled high with letters from all over the world, for her books and articles and poems were being published in England and France and Germany, and word of her work for the seamen was being carried to every port. Each morning the first thing she did was run through the mail, placing it in neat piles to be answered. She answered every letter personally and by hand.

One autumn morning in 1836 she discovered in the heap of correspondence a letter with a special, businesslike appearance. She opened it with only slight curiosity, but as she read her cheeks flushed with pleasure. Once before she had received a similar letter—and it had changed her entire life. It had changed her from an unknown, poor country house-wife to a world-recognized, well-to-do, and influential edi-tress. She was thinking of this as she reread the letter.

She was still studying the communication when the door of her office opened and in strode James Dow, her employer. Dow saw the look of absorption on his chief employee's face.

"Anything wrong?" he asked.

Sarah shook her head. "No. Nothing is wrong. I was just wondering what I should say in tactfully refusing this offer." She held the letter out and the publisher took it. As he read, a frown creased his brow.

"The gall of that fellow!" he growled. "Trying to steal you away."

Sarah's clear laugh rang out. "You know that no one can

steal me away! But it is flattering, isn't it? Flattering to our *American Ladies' Magazine* that the great Godey comes to it for an editress? Godey, the Prince of Publishers, I think he's sometimes called."

"He wants to wreck us, that's what he wants. We're too much competition for him, Prince or no Prince! He's been trying for years to imitate us—now he's given up and wants to take you away and thus kill us off entirely." Dow's face was red with anger.

Sarah, hating to see any man's equanimity disturbed, rose and came around the desk to Dow's side. "Don't worry," she said gently. "I have no intention of leaving our magazine."

She answered the letter from Louis Godey, the prominent Philadelphia publisher, telling him firmly that she could not consider his offer to become editress of his *Lady's Book*.

"This has been my home for nearly ten years," she explained. "I am deeply involved in many civic and welfare projects here, and my two sons are attending Harvard. I cannot leave, no matter how attractive your offer."

Sarah sealed the letter, pressing down the wafer of wax with the conviction that this was the end of the matter. But she was reckoning without Louis Godey. She knew, of course, his history as a publisher and his reputation in the journalistic world. As a rival and actually an imitator of her own work, he had been watched carefully ever since that first issue of his *Lady's Book* which John Putnam had shown her six years ago.

Louis Godey, sixteen years younger than Sarah, had been born in New York City in 1804. There, as a young man, he had set up a bookshop and magazine stand, which he had operated until 1828. In that year, just a few months after Sarah had started work on the *Ladies' Magazine*, Godey left New York and went to Philadelphia, where he, too, embarked on a journalistic career. For two years he worked in minor positions, learning the publishing business from the editorial room through the composing room and the binding and distributing. He studied the business end as well, and mastered the art of making a magazine pay a profit. At the end of those two years he felt that he was ready to publish his own magazine.

By that time the *Ladies' Magazine* in Boston was making itself felt in the world. Godey wanted to publish a similar journal, but one that would be somewhat more sophisticated, with a nation-wide rather than a regional appeal. He felt that from Philadelphia, then the publishing center of the country, a magazine for women would have a better chance for wide circulation.

For six years he had watched Sarah and had tried to out-guess and out-edit her—to produce a magazine that would put the Boston journal to shame. But he had been forced to admit that he could not do it. He was a businessman, a publisher, and, although he enjoyed writing, he was not hitting the mark he was aiming at. The only thing to do was to hire Mrs. Hale. Together they could produce a winner.

In recent months, every issue of Godey's *Lady's Book* had carried complimentary references to Sarah and her work. In September the wily Godey had gone so far as to publish a poem written by Sarah's son Horatio, even though it was not very good. Sarah had been aware of these sly overtures, but she had not been prepared for the handsome offer made in his recent letter. Nor was she prepared for the result of her refusal.

She lifted her eyes from her writing one day as a young, determined-looking man was ushered into her office. He stood in front of Sarah's desk, his feet wide apart, as he regarded her quizzically with keen gray eyes. Then he spoke in a booming voice:

"Mrs. Hale! You are just as I imagined you—entirely feminine, beautiful, winsome. How! But you don't know me——"

"Indeed!" Sarah said, smiling, some instinct giving her the clue, "Indeed I do know you, Mr. Godey. Won't you please be seated?"

Godey chuckled. "I should have known it. You have a sixth sense, Mrs. Hale." He stretched out his hand and Sarah, rising, took it. She came only a little past his shoulder, and she had to tilt back her head to smile up into the gray eyes. Godey held her small hand and beamed down at her.

"Surely, now that I have come all the way from Philadelphia, you will have luncheon with me?"

"Of course, Mr. Godey. But let me warn you beforehand: Luncheon will buy you nothing. I am determined not to leave Boston."

They had a merry meal, Godey displaying all the charm and wit he possessed. Sarah found herself liking him very much. She felt sure that they could work harmoniously together, but she shook her brown curls decidedly.

She smiled at her companion as they finished luncheon. "I am truly sorry," she said, "but my decision is firm."

"Well, I will escort you back to your office—and then we'll see," the Philadelphian answered genially.

Sarah had not been back at her desk an hour before James Dow and Louis Godey came into her office. Dow spoke without preamble.

"Mrs. Hale, you must be the first to know this: I have just sold the *Ladies' Magazine* to Mr. Godey."

Sarah's quill pen dropped from her fingers. She raised

shocked eyes toward the man she had thought so pleasant and open.

"Mr. Godey! How could you do such a thing?"

Godey stepped over to her desk and leaned toward her flushed face. "I must have you as my editress," he said simply. "And if this is the only way I can get you, this is the way it must be."

Sarah turned to Dow. "But what will happen to our magazine?"

"It is Godey's now," he answered, "to do with as he pleases."

"It will be consolidated with my own *Lady's Book*—and you will be the editress," Godey declared.

Suddenly Sarah's eyes flashed. She rose to her feet, standing erect and angry. "I have told you, Mr. Godey, I will not leave Boston."

Godey chuckled good-naturedly. "As you wish, my dear. Stay here if it pleases you, for I want you to be happy. But edit my book—that is all I ask."

Sarah's resistance collapsed before his friendly determination. She sat back in her chair and considered. Finally she raised luminous eyes to the publisher's face. "Very well, Mr. Godey, you win. But this must be understood: I must have as free a hand as I have always had. I cannot work unless I am free to put my own ideas into the magazine."

Godey beamed. "That's exactly what I want, my dear. Exactly!" He rubbed his plump hands together gleefully. "Now we'll show the world what a real magazine is!"

9

MISSION ACCOMPLISHED

GODEY RETURNED TO PHILADELPHIA MIGHTILY PLEASED
with himself. The next issue of the *Lady's Book*, December,
1836, carried the triumphant announcement:

> The present number of the *Lady's Book* closes our career as
> sole editor. . . . We are confident that our readers will not
> regret this change when they learn that Mrs. Sarah Josepha
> Hale, late editor of the *American Ladies' Magazine* (which
> work is now amalgamated with the *Lady's Book*) will superin-
> tend the literary department of the Book. Mrs. Hale is too well
> known to the public to need eulogy from us. For nine years
> she has conducted the magazine, which she originated, how! its
> readers well know . . .

One word in the announcement pleased Sarah more than
all the rest. Mr. Godey had called her an "editor," not
"editress." It sounded fine to her ears, which were sensitive
to catch any word or phrase that indicated the acceptance of
women in competition with men.

Sarah was not insensible to the honor of being chosen for
the editorship of Godey's *Lady's Book;* nor was she unaware
of the tremendously enlarged audience she would now com-

mand and of her greater opportunities for working to promote the welfare of women. But Boston had become home to her and to her children, and she refused to leave the city that had bestowed so many rewards upon her work.

She believed she could edit the *Lady's Book* from Boston, in spite of all the handicaps of distance. There were three hundred and fifty miles of stage road to be covered, roads mired in mud, or slippery with ice and snow, or fetlock-deep in dust—according to the season. Of course, from New York the work could go on to Philadelphia by boat, but that, too, was slow. Sarah felt that she could write her editorials and book reviews far enough in advance of publication date to cause no delay, but it meant a great deal of work, and she would have to trust the proofreading to others. This worried her, for she had always taken care to examine the proofs before the final printing of the magazine.

She went right to work, however, and the January, 1837 issue of the *Lady's Book* came out on schedule, with Sarah's declaration of policy featured. She told her new readers—and the old ones—that she meant to carry on her former policies of promoting the welfare of women, encouraging new inventions that would ease their labor in the home, publishing the latest styles and the newest designs for needlework, as well as recipes, book reviews, and the other popular features she had inaugurated.

That spring Horatio was graduated from Harvard. He had shown a remarkable talent for languages, and had, some time before graduation, received a signal honor. He had been chosen to act as philologist on the United States Exploring Expedition under Captain Charles Wilkes. Involved as she was with her new work and all her charitable activities, Sarah nevertheless entered enthusiastically into her son's preparation for the exciting trip. The expedition was to leave during the summer, and planned to visit South America, New South Wales, the Samoan Islands, and then proceed down into the Antarctic. It was the first such expedition sent out by the government, and everyone connected with it was filled with eager anticipation.

Then in June, over in England, Victoria was crowned queen, and the new sovereign provided Sarah with an excellent topic for the magazine. Not only was Victoria a woman, and therefore of intense interest to Sarah, but she promised to be a good ruler and to end the debauchery and cruelty and inefficiency that had long marked the royal family. Sarah wrote many glowing tributes to the young queen and did not hesitate to predict a long and glorious reign for her.

The Christmas season of 1838 was a happy one for the family, in spite of the fact that Horatio was absent. David came home on leave, tanned and seemingly strong after his outdoor life in Florida. Frances and Josepha were on vacation from Mrs. Willard's seminary, and William, the "baby" of the family, was a tall young sophomore at Harvard.

Always an enthusiastic observer of holidays, Sarah entered into this one with special joy. The Boston house was decorated with holly and mistletoe, and the tables and sideboard were heaped with good things to eat. The fire glowed in the fireplace, and the candles glimmered on the mantel as the five happy members of the family gathered each evening to chat and sing. And though the singing might begin with the new popular favorites, "The Old Oaken Bucket" and "Home, Sweet Home," it always ended with some of Sarah's little songs. Sarah's heart swelled with emotion as she looked at these four handsome young people and heard their clear voices sing the song she had taught them so many years ago, when they were just babies at her knee:

"Our Father in Heaven
We hallow thy name!
May thy kingdom so holy
On earth be the same—
O give to us daily,
Our portion of bread!
It is from thy bounty
That all must be fed.

"Forgive our transgressions,
And teach us to know
That humble compassion
That pardons each foe—
Keep us from temptation,
From weakness and sin—
And thine be the glory
Forever—Amen!"

The happy holidays were scarcely over when David met his mother at the door one January afternoon as she returned rather late from the office. In his hand he held a letter and on his face was a look of regret.

"Mother," he began at once, "my leave is up. These are my orders to join my company. We are being sent to the Canadian border——"

Sarah sighed. "I feared this would come ever since I learned of the trouble up there. But I was hoping it could be settled without our interference."

David helped his mother remove her cloak and bonnet, keeping his face turned away as he answered, "It might have been if those New Yorkers hadn't taken it into their heads to help the Canadians fight for independence. After all, it was none of their affair."

Sarah laid her hand gently on his arm. "No, David. Yet, I suppose that when the neighboring Americans learned that Canada was dissatisfied with the treatment it was getting, they remembered our own Revolution and wanted to help. And, you know, it might be best for Canada to throw off the British yoke and become one with us."

"I know that, Mother, but the New Yorkers were acting without authority. They just seized Navy Island in the Niagara River and fortified it on their own hook. And then, when the loyal Canadians tried to retake the island—well, you know what happened. So now, in mid-winter, Uncle Sam has to send soldiers up there to settle the trouble."

Sarah was silent, remembering all the excitement there had been when the Canadians had set fire to the *Caroline,* the supply ship of the adventurers, and had sent it in flames over Niagara Falls. What an outcry had arisen! What demands to punish Great Britain for this act!

Frances Ann had come into the room to hear David's last words. "But, David, it's winter and so cold up there! And you have been down in Florida, where it is warm. Why can't they send troops accustomed to the cold?"

Sarah smiled a gentle rebuke at her daughter. "David is a soldier, Fanny. He goes where he is sent." But she felt a sudden tug at her heart, and her hand on David's arm was trembling.

Sarah's fears and Frances' questions were justified a few months later when word came to Sarah that her eldest son was dead. The change from the warm Everglades of Florida to the icy plains of the Canadian border had indeed proved too much, not only for David, but for many of his comrades in General Wool's command. David had been rushed to the new army hospital at Plattsburg, New York, near the Canadian border, where he had died on April 30.

Sarah felt that she could not bear this blow. David had been more than a son. Ever since his father's death he had been companion and friend and confidant. For him to die away from home, racked with coughing, his lungs and heart bursting, was too cruel. After his body was brought home and buried in the Boston cemetery, Sarah went on with her work, silently grieving.

Louis Godey understood her sorrow and felt that it would be wise for her to leave Boston after the tragic climax to her happy years there. But Sarah could not yet face a new life. She wrote to the compassionate Godey, "It is not a common loss that I mourn. . . . I depended on him as a friend . . . . I cannot, at once, summon the fortitude to enter on the occupations of a world so dark and desolate as this now appears."

But Sarah's strong sense of duty came to her assistance. She would not permit herself to fail in her obligation to her employer, and each month she carried on the strenuous, detailed work of her job. She realized that her writing had lost its buoyancy, but she kept her pen moving across the paper, forcing her mind to function and her grief to be silent.

William was graduated from Harvard in the spring of 1840, second in his class, again proving the effectiveness of Sarah's methods of teaching. Now she was free to move to Philadelphia, save for one thing—the Bunker Hill Monument again.

A few days before William's graduation Sarah had found on her desk the annual report of the Monument Association. She was only slightly curious. For the last ten years the report had been the same discouraged account of failure to raise funds. But as she read this year's record, irritation mounted in her. For one thing, it referred to her Seaman's Aid Society as a "female sewing society of Boston."

"Sewing society, indeed!" Sarah muttered. "That is actually slanderous, after all we've done. And utterly ignoring our Mariners' House, our schools, nurseries, and libraries—and the fact that we are the first and the largest women's organization in the country!"

She laid the report down, her small fist clenched upon it. "We ought to show them! We could do it now. Ten years ago we failed, but now . . . well, I've learned many things and so have the women of America."

She had the confidence now of the successful, influential individual, and the backing of one of the most widely read magazines in the country. The thought of such power produced a glow of satisfaction and a feeling of derring-do that for a moment almost muffled her year-old grief. As she lay awake that night, she began to make her plans. She would go about this in a different manner from her timid pleas for money of ten years ago.

By the time of William's graduation she was deep in her project. It was so daring, so unheard-of, that it stimulated Sarah to enthusiastic effort. She would promote a fair—such as the country had never beheld. It would be sponsored solely by women and would display and sell only the work of women from all parts of the country. And the proceeds would be given to the Monument Association. Maybe that would stir the men up to finish the job they had abandoned!

She outlined her plan in a letter to Godey:

The advantages will be manifold. We'll increase the interest in the Book, for both men and women will take notice. Then we'll show that women can do things—but we'll keep their activities to the age-old sphere of women so that the men can raise no objections. The Fair will show what the American women can do in the way of needlework and sewing, cooking and preserving and pickling. And there will be other activities—. I am confident that we can raise a substantial fund toward the completion of the Monument, which has stood as an eyesore and reproach for so long.

Godey, reading the letter, grinned. "And you'll do it too, my dear."

The next issue of the *Book* announced the project in such glowing terms that the women readers leaped into action. An avalanche of enthusiastic letters poured across Sarah's desk; women set right to work to make Sarah's fair the outstanding event of the year. For the next three months women in every section of the country worked as they had never worked before—with joy and pride in what their needles and stoves, their minds and imaginations could produce. Knitting needles were clicking, thimbles clacking, preserve kettles bubbling, and ovens sending out tempting aromas. Among the more fashionable women there were classes in making wax and hair flowers, in crayon painting, and other ladylike pursuits.

The Monument Fair opened in Quincy Hall, the largest auditorium in Boston, on September 8, 1840, to run for one week. The opening day presented a spectacle such as Boston had never seen. Still modestly dressed in dark silk, but with cheeks aglow with pride, Sarah stood in the receiving line with a score of the most prominent women of the city. She was graciousness itself, especially to the men who came to make fun and stayed to admire the beautifully decorated hall and the marvelous display of women's work.

That evening Sarah read what the newspapers had to say about the event and she smiled with pleasure, for every report praised the women and their work. The *Evening Transcript* went into raptures: "The Exhibition is indescribably magnificent, and far surpasses anything of the kind ever before got up in this city."

Another report declared, "The finest spirit animates every breast. The ladies are all attention—all smiles—all civility. . . . The view as one enters is bewitching in the extreme."

When the final report was ready, after totaling the receipts and deducting the expenses, Sarah was even happier. Her Monument Fair had cleared over thirty thousand dollars! Spurred on by this generous contribution to the Fund, two wealthy former Bostonians sent in ten thousand dollars each; other men raised five thousand dollars—and there it was: fifty-five thousand dollars. Enough to complete the monument. And the women had done the biggest share.

Sarah felt that she could leave Boston now. She had successfully completed most of the projects she had planned. The women of the city were alert to their problems and instructed in ways of progress. She was ready for Philadelphia.

======o=o======= 10

A PLACE IN THE SUN

On a cold, blustery day early in the year 1841 the stagecoach from New York came bowling along the cobbled streets of Philadelphia. The horses stepped carefully over the slippery stones, the harness bells jingled in the crisp air, while the driver, muffled to his ears, cracked his whip smartly. He gave a grunt of satisfaction as he drew the teams to a halt in front of the little two-story red brick building on Third Street, and "Admiral" Jim Reeside, the stage-line contractor, came puffing out to open the coach doors and help down the weary passengers.

The Admiral, as he was known throughout the Quaker City, was a huge man, and this was his job. But today he was shouldered aside by a tall, plump man, overcoated and mufflered, with small eyes twinkling above round, rosy cheeks. The newcomer muttered an apology, but the Admiral merely grinned.

"Meeting someone, eh?" he asked.

"Yes. How!" Louis Godey answered, his voice muffled by the great woolen scarf around neck and chin. "I do hope she is on this coach!"

At that moment a small, fur-cloaked figure appeared in the coach doorway, and Godey leaped forward. "Mrs. Hale!" he almost shouted.

Loungers looked up at the name, and the Admiral chuckled. "No wonder you were in such a hurry, sir!"

Sarah's smile lit up her pale oval face, wiping away the traces of weariness lightly etched on her smooth cheeks.

"Mr. Godey, sir! This is a happy surprise!"

"Surprise nothing! You must have known, my dear, that I would meet you. I am so glad that you have come at last . . ."

Sarah smiled and raised her candid eyes to her employer. "Yes," she admitted frankly, "I suppose I did know. But it's very kind of you, nevertheless. On such a cold day."

His hand under her elbow, the publisher directed Sarah across the slick cobblestones to his waiting carriage.

"It's been a wonderful journey, but so long!" Sarah said as she settled back in the comfortable cushions. "I came partway, you know, by the new Western Railroad. The line from Boston to Albany has just been finished. Then down the Hudson by boat to New York." She paused. "What a city New York is! You know, sir, I have done so little traveling in my life. This has been a real adventure."

"You bear traveling very well," her companion said admiringly. "You look as fresh as a daisy!"

Sarah shook her head, smiling. Mr. Godey was so exuberant! It would be stimulating to work with that enthusiasm buoying her up all the time. She looked out at the street through which they were traveling.

"What a pretty city this is!" she exclaimed. "The red brick houses, all so neat and prim and standing in such straight rows. Our Boston streets, you know, are the crookedest and narrowest in the whole country. Those clean white steps and shining brass knockers—and are those numbers, sir?"

"Oh yes, my dear. The houses in Philadelphia are all numbered—it makes the delivery of mail and the finding of people so much easier."

Sarah nodded thoughtfully. "Our business houses are numbered, of course, but only a few residences."

"Wait till spring," Godey said enthusiastically. "Wait till the trees are green along the Delaware and Schuylkill and Wissahickon. In the spring the rivers are lovely and the grass and trees around our fine public buildings . . ."

"I'm going to see them all. I love Boston because of its intimate connection with our nation's history. And Philadelphia is even more closely identified with the birth of our country. I must get to know every historic spot."

"But we have no Bunker Hill Monument for you to battle over."

"Maybe there'll be something else—your Congress Hall?" Sarah teased.

Godey grinned wryly. "That's something of a shrine already. At least it's visited every day by scores of people. The post office is housed there."

His bright eyes regarded the woman seated beside him. Under her fur cloak she wore a plain woolen dress. Her brown hair fell in curls from under her little bonnet, her cheeks were firm and unlined. Could she really be fifty-two years old?

Sarah raised her eyes and caught the quizzical expression on her employer's face. "No, this is not the latest fashion from Godey's *Lady's Book*," she said pleasantly. "But the latest fashions do not suit me and, as I advise my readers every month, a woman should adopt only those styles which suit her own personality."

Godey laid his plump hand on her arm. "You are quite right, my dear. How! If every woman had your good sense . . ." he sighed.

"There would be little need for a lady editor!"

As she sat there, riding through the snowy Philadelphia streets, Sarah's thoughts were as clear as the sparkling air outside the carriage. She might be dressed in the simple, old-fashioned style that she felt was most becoming to her—a style that added height to her tiny figure, dignity to her daintiness. Her hair might be done in the fashion of the 1820's, but she was not the inexperienced, simple country woman she had been when she went to Boston. Now she was a woman of business and of ample means, cultivated, assured, with more power over the public mind than any other woman of the day. She had been sought out to come here and take her place in the sun.

Sarah was serenely conscious of her power. Her success with the Seaman's Aid Society with all its ramifications, her triumph with the Monument Fair, had put the crowning stamp on the position she had been acquiring ever since that first timid editorial in the *Ladies' Magazine*. Other magazines had aped her policies and her innovations and had tried to outguess her next forward step, but none had succeeded. For there was no one else who seemed to understand the hopes and longings of American women—hopes and longings and ambitions never before spoken aloud. Sarah was their spokesman, courageous and unflinching.

Her mind was already leaping ahead to the problems she would attack here. Philadelphia, like Boston, was a seaport. There would be plenty of opportunity to extend her seamen's aid, her libraries and schools for their families. In the vast publishing activity of the city there should be many jobs that could be filled by women. And there was housing—on her journey down from Boston she had passed through many villages and had shuddered at the ugly farmhouses. And in the cities she had been horrified at the tenements and slums. All America needed awakening to the need for better homes. Oh, there was plenty to be done.

"I believe I am going to like it here," Sarah said at last.

Godey chuckled. "And Philadelphia is going to like you, my dear."

Godey was right. Philadelphia was as captivated by Sarah as she was by the historic Quaker City. Louis Godey had already arranged for Sarah's accommodation at one of the more elegant boardinghouses of the prosperous city. To this house his carriage now took her, and she was introduced to the family with whom she would make her home for some years. The landlady was properly impressed at having the famous editress as one of her boarders, and she fluttered about Sarah with an eager attention that amused Godey.

"Rest today, my dear," the publisher said expansively as he fiddled with the gold watch chain across his ample waist-coat. "Tomorrow, if you feel up to it, I'll call for you and take you down to the office."

Sarah smiled, good humor wiping out the weariness that shadowed her eyes. "I'm eager to see where I am going to work and to meet those with whom I shall be employed. But a few hours' rest will be very welcome."

As Godey left, Sarah sighed. Such enthusiasm and vitality! She hoped that a good night's rest would give her back her customary energy, which was somewhat depleted by the fatiguing journey from Boston.

Sarah had scarcely closed her eyes that night when she was brought sharply awake by the clang of bells and the shouting of people. She sat up in bed to listen to the rattle of wheels and the clanking of harness, punctuated by yells. She hurried to her window and looked out. Then she realized what it was: a volunteer fire company rushing to answer an alarm. The great bell at Congress Hall clanged out the signal that told the men in which quarter of the city the flames were raging; it was answered by bugles rousing the men; and these brought out the companies in all the uproarious hubbub of the glorious activity.

Several times during the night the same commotion awakened her, and she began to wonder whether she could ever adjust to the noise and activity of a Philadelphia night. At last, toward morning, utterly exhausted, she fell into slumber so deep that even the fire bells failed to rouse her. When she did awaken, it was to find that it was past nine o'clock. She arose and hurriedly made herself ready for this important day.

She had scarcely finished breakfast when Godey arrived to take her down to his Utopia—the building where his beloved *Lady's Book* was prepared and printed.

Sarah donned cloak and bonnet, went out into the cold, crisp air, and Godey assisted her into the carriage with its spanking team of well-fed, gleaming horses. She settled back in the velvet-upholstered seat, and Godey climbed in beside her.

"Well, my dear," he said, "are you ready to take your place in the sun? You were hidden up there in Boston. Here, in the hub of the publishing world, you can really shine!"

Sarah smiled quietly and leaned forward to peer out at the streets, already athrong with moving people, carriages, and wagons.

Down along Chestnut Street they traveled, while Sarah craned her neck to look at the shop windows as they whirled by, and to wonder at the hustle and bustle. As they neared the famous Publishers' Row, the crowd grew denser, and

Sarah smiled to see the beaver-hatted, woolen-mufflered gentlemen hastening to work.

"So many people—all in such a hurry!" she exclaimed.

"It won't be long until you'll be saying 'Good Morning' to most of these hurrying men. They are publishers and writers, artists and engravers—and they'll all be flocking to Godey's as soon as they know that my charming editress has arrived."

Godey's office was at 113 Chestnut Street, not far from the river front and in the very heart of the publishing district. As the carriage stopped and Godey assisted Sarah to the sidewalk, she gazed about her with eager interest.

"The very air seems to smell of printer's ink!" she exclaimed. "I already feel my fingers itching to grasp a pen and begin work."

"You'll give new life to the *Book*—and to the office as well, my dear! We'll make history here. How!"

Sarah turned her head so that the man would not see the amused smile that twisted her lips at hearing this favorite expression. Already, in the two times she had met him before this, she had grown to expect that explosive syllable whenever Godey was excited. Even in his letters and in his column in the *Book*, he could not avoid punctuating his statements with that exclamation: *How!*

Once inside the building, Sarah found that Godey's was much like the Boston office—busy, noisy, cluttered. The employees stopped whatever they were doing and clustered around, eager to meet in person the famous editress, who for over four years had been conducting her work from Boston. Sarah was the very soul of graciousness and tact. She shook hands with each employee, repeating the name with a brief word or two. Later, when she had reason to speak to anyone, she addressed the individual by name, always correctly. This little nicety made her immediately popular with them all.

For his prized editress Godey had prepared a large, clean office on the second floor, with windows that looked down upon busy Chestnut Street. When Sarah had gratefully acknowledged this kindness, she removed her cloak and bonnet and stepped to the window. She felt that she was going to love the bustling thoroughfare below her. As her eyes studied it, she noticed a shop across the street, where a large, shaggy black bear stood on his hind legs in the window. After her first gasp she realized that it was a stuffed bear, but she was intrigued.

"Oh Mr. Godey," she exclaimed, "what on earth is that, sir?"

Godey, peering over her shoulder, chuckled. "That's Philadelphia's most famous sweet shop: Roussel's—Eugene Roussel's. Last summer he set up a newfangled gadget, claimed it was the only one in America. He calls it a soda fountain—and a sort of fountain it really is, my dear. He presses a spigot and out gushes a cool, frothy drink—not at all intoxicating either! He calls it soda water. Or one may get beef-and-iron tonic or sarsaparilla. He did a tremendous business during the hot weather, and even now, cold as it is, he still does a brisk trade. I must take you over there and introduce you, my dear. It's a very stylish place—you'll meet all the ladies of fashion there."

Sarah turned away from the window and went to the huge desk on which already were lying the proof sheets of the next issue of the *Lady's Book*. She did not pick these up immediately, for her eye was caught by a pile of Graham's *Gentleman's Magazine* on one end of her desk. She picked up a copy, with its engraving of Benjamin Franklin on the frontispiece. She turned the pages, studying them, though she was well acquainted with this journal, as she was with all competitors.

"That's going to be our big problem," Godey said, watching her. "Since Rex Graham hired Edgar Poe as editor, his circulation has been mounting at an alarming rate. And of course you've seen the complimentary notices in the New York papers."

Sarah nodded. "Yes, I've seen them. And, of course, I know Mr. Poe's ability. I think I was one of the first editors to whom he sent work—back when he was a cadet at West Point. And even though he may offer us some rough competition, I'm very glad that he has a steady job now. And it must be a remunerative one. He has always had such a difficult time . . ."

"Remunerative!" Godey snorted. "It's an open secret along the row that Rex promised Poe a good salary but he hasn't paid it. Poe isn't getting what he's worth to Graham, by any means!"

Sarah's eyes were troubled. "I'm sorry if that's true. Graham's magazine didn't amount to much before Poe took it over——"

Godey grunted. "Well, let's not worry about that, my dear. Mr. Poe will surely be in to see you. He makes the rounds of all the offices quite regularly. And when good weather comes, you'll see him sitting under the canopy at the corner of Dock and Lodge streets. He doesn't seem to be either very prosperous or very happy—though both he and Mrs. Poe seem better off than when they came to Philadelphia three years ago."

Sarah sat down at her desk, smoothing down her full skirt as she settled herself for work. She was again clad in her customary dark silk dress—the material she habitually wore because it shed the dust of the office and always looked elegant.

"I'll leave you now, my dear," Godey said, going to the door. "My office is right next to yours. Do not hesitate to call on me if you need anything or want to discuss something."

Sarah smiled serenely, already feeling quite at home. "Thank you, sir. It looks as if there is plenty of work waiting for me."

The next days and weeks were filled to overflowing with activity. Sarah not only had to read every contribution, decide which should be accepted, and then reread and edit them; she also had to review books, write letters to correspondents, decide on payment for material, and select many of the illustrations used. Most of this work she was used to—it was what she had done on the old *Ladies' Magazine*, and for Godey as well.

But here there were calls upon her time such as she had never known before. In Boston, most of the contributions had come to her desk through the post. She had had little personal contact with authors and artists. Here, almost all the work was done through personal interviews. Authors, artists, engravers, printers—everyone who had any connection with the *Book* worked nearby and constantly came bustling into Sarah's office to consult her. Many who had no real business with Godey's manufactured an excuse so that they could see and speak to the lady editress, whose fame had preceded her to the city. All this consumed a great deal of time and energy.

One of her first activities was to make herself intimately acquainted with the physical plant and the workers there. As she went through the various editorial offices, the composing room, the folding and binding quarters, the distributing center, she took in every detail. It was no news to her that all this work was done by hand—but the presses here were of a much later type than those she had been used to, and the work proceeded with much greater speed.

Sarah was looking for something definite: Where could she put women to work in the production of the *Book*? There were many jobs, she saw, that women could do with greater speed and efficiency than men. The coloring of the fashion plates was one detail that was ideally suited to the abilities and skills of women. As soon as she could, Sarah persuaded Godey to employ women for this work. It was a tremendous undertaking to color by hand each plate for thousands of magazines. Much of this coloring was done in one big room at the plant, but a large part was "farmed out" for women to do in their homes.

The addressing of the bundles of magazines and of individual copies was another hand-done task that was suitable for women, and Sarah soon had dozens of girls, their sleeves covered with black armlets, sitting at long tables neatly writing out the address labels.

When anyone attempted to criticize her for replacing men with women workers, Sarah had her answer ready:

"Every woman in our employ needs the work and the money. She is either a mother—a widow—supporting her family, or a young girl forced by circumstance to earn her own way. Such women are just as entitled to a share in remunerative labor as are men similarly placed."

Whether the objector agreed or not, Godey went on employing women—and the women repaid the *Book* with a fierce loyalty.

In publishing, Philadelphia had a long-standing lead over other cities. This lead dated from the time Benjamin Franklin had brought from England the best type and presses then available, which provided Philadelphia's printing houses with facilities a hundred years in advance of those in other cities. This lead had continued through generations of publishers, printers, and bookbinders. Here had been published the first American editions of Shakespeare, Milton, and Goldsmith, the first English Bible to be printed in this country, the first American religious journal, and the first American daily newspaper.

To Sarah, all this was stimulating. She felt as if she never before had really been a magazine editor, as if she had emerged from dim and solitary confinement into the sunshine and warmth and companionship of a busy neighborhood.

Not only Publishers' Row but the entire city fascinated her. The neat cobbled streets, laid out at right angles to each other, were so different from Boston's "wandering cow tracks." The whole city had a freshly scrubbed air, due in part to the faucets at all the front doors. Sarah was intrigued by these faucets, which provided strong streams of water with which the doorways and steps and sidewalks were scrubbed each morning. Sarah heartily approved of the city's water system, the finest in the country, though it made her cringe inwardly to see women, swathed in huge aprons, scrubbing the sidewalks.

It was not long before Sarah visited Independence Hall, where the Declaration of Independence had been signed. She stood with awe in Congress Hall, where Washington had delivered his moving "Farewell Address" and where the United States Congress had met when Philadelphia was the nation's first capital. There were other historical sights to see: Holy Trinity Church, which Washington had attended; Franklin's grave; Franklin's tomb; and statues of Robert Morris, William Penn, and other men who had helped to shape the nation. Sometimes Sarah felt that she could not absorb all the poignant history epitomized in this city.

Quite different in its appeal to Sarah was the market place, which she loved to visit. Often she arose early in the morning so that she could stroll through the busy square, reveling in its noises and sights. She loved the aroma of the big brown crocks of country butter, the spicy loaves of pumpernickel and rye bread, the great, round cheeses. The hearty Dutch food was different from New England's fare—richer, spicier, with a warm fragrance that stirred the appetite.

There were also the familiar foods: turkey, quail, and venison; rosy apples and, in season, huge bunches of purple grapes—Isabellas from the surrounding farms or Concords that reminded Sarah of home.

It seemed to Sarah that, in Philadelphia, marketing was a social activity. Here at the heaped-up stalls she could see society ladies in all their finery, choosing fruits and meats and vegetables while a liveried coachman stood waiting to carry the purchases to the carriage. Soberly dressed Quakers, ruddy-faced Dutch housewives, and calico-clad mothers with children clinging to their skirts, jostled and laughed good-naturedly. There must be some who did not care to join in the fun of market day, Sarah thought, for adding color to the scene were yellow- and red-turbaned Negresses, servants of the wealthy families, selecting eggs and butter and cheese with the greatest solemnity and care.

Alert as she was to all things pertaining to the daily life of women, Sarah found the market place stimulating and exciting. She would go to her desk and write of what she saw—of the foods that were plentiful and so reasonably priced; of new ways to handle and to preserve perishable fruits; of the sensible dress of the farm women. Sarah found something on every excursion to pass on to her eager readers—something to praise or perhaps something to condemn or warn them against.

In this unremitting crush of activity, Sarah was able to forget her grief over David's death and her loneliness at being separated from her children. As she had done before, she met the challenge of the new situation, this time with confidence born of success.

The challenge was like a tonic, energizing her spirit, enlivening her imagination. Sitting at her desk, nibbling the end of her quill pen, Sarah recalled what Godey had said about taking her place in the sun. Here she was, among the giants of the publishing world—and she was not falling behind in the race for recognition.

THE BATTLE OF THE GIANTS

GODEY'S *Lady's Book* AND GRAHAM'S *Gentleman's Magazine*, the two giants of the journalistic world, were squarely pitted against each other, while the publishers of lesser "books" seemed content to sit back and watch the battle. Entrenched in their offices only a few blocks apart, Louis Antoine Godey and George Rex Graham pondered the moves that would win in the contest for circulation, while their two editors managed the campaign in their own, very different ways.

Sarah knew her adversary. She remembered the letters from David at West Point, urging her to purchase the poems of his erratic classmate. And, while the editor in Sarah rejected the strange and exotic rhythms, the writer in her recognized an undoubted genius. Having to return the poems had troubled Sarah, and she had thus reasoned with herself:

"After all, I am trying to produce a magazine that will appeal to women—all women, I hope!—and I am sure that very, very few would enjoy or get any meaning at all out of these strange syllables. My aim is to awaken women to their needs and their rights. Every word I print should help in some way to further this aim." She sighed. "I am quite sure these poems would not help."

Later Poe had sent her other poems and stories, and some she had been able to purchase, while others had again been returned to the author. Before leaving Boston, Sarah had written high praise of Poe's book, *Tales of the Grotesque and Arabesque.* Her review, appearing in Godey's *Book* in January of 1840, had helped greatly in selling the little volume, for at that time Godey's was claimed to have the largest circulation of any magazine in the world.

But that was more than a year before Sarah's arrival in Philadelphia. In that year Graham had employed Poe as his editor, and Godey's beloved *Book* was facing its first real competition. Poe was proving to be an excellent editor—but one that appealed more to the intelligent and the cultivated than to the masses. Sarah realized that Poe had many advantages: he was a man, filling a role traditionally limited to men. He had genius. Sarah was too capable and too experienced not to recognize these points; but if she had not seen them for herself, the literary critics would have made her aware of them—especially the New York critics, who hailed Graham's journal as a magazine of good taste and fine literary quality, while at the same time they loved to poke fun at Godey's *Book.*

Godey's round cheeks would mottle with an angry surge of blood when he read such comments as "It lacks both dignity and sense." But Sarah did not let such phrases ruffle her serenity.

"I have grown used to criticism," she pointed out calmly. "Ever since I began editing the *Ladies' Magazine,* editors have taken pot shots at me. But do you not notice, sir, that our circulation is not harmed by such remarks? The women love our *Book,* and any criticism of it seems to be a criticism of their taste. This makes them resentful and determined to defend their choice. In fact, sir, I have learned that circulation grows almost in proportion to adverse comment."

"You are right as always, my dear. But 'neither dignity nor sense'! I find it hard to swallow that." He picked up one of Graham's magazines and riffled through the pages, a frown between his brows. "Do they really think that these dull stories are of better quality than those we publish?"

"They are of a different quality, sir." Sarah's own taste had been refined by her association with her husband and with the best writers of the time, and she had to admit to herself that she liked the stories Poe wrote and the ones he bought from others. But she didn't want to publish the same kind.

"Mr. Poe is aiming at a critical readership; we are aiming to entertain and instruct women. And there are many more women than there are literary critics, sir. Our circulation is still ahead of Graham's, isn't it?"

"It is. How! But Graham's is coming along—more than twenty thousand subscribers now. Still, we can honestly claim to have the largest circulation of any magazine."

"And I propose to keep it that way," Sarah said firmly.

What more could she do for her readers? Why not something practical in the way of encouraging inventors to produce machines to lighten women's work? That should interest both men and women. She would give full and complete accounts of any such machines, and perhaps, in time, she could persuade Godey to offer cash awards to the inventors.

Pursuing this thought, she kept abreast of the work being done by Walter Hunt in New York City where he was trying to perfect a sewing machine. Hunt's efforts resulted in a machine for "sewing, stitching and seaming cloth," though it could sew only a straight seam a few inches long. As soon as it became known that such a device was feasible, a great outcry arose. It would deprive hundreds of women of their means of livelihood. Sewing was one of the few occupations open to them, but such a machine would make their work unnecessary and they would have to starve or beg. It must never be manufactured! Hearing the outcry, Hunt refused to go on with his project.

"American women must know I want to help them, not harm them," he said sadly. "It was to help them that I invented the safety pin—no one can say that little gadget has done mothers any harm! And I was hoping that this sewing machine would lighten their work. I hoped that they would not be like the French, who put an end to Thimonnier's experiments along this line back in the early 'thirties. But if the women do not want my machine, I shall not manufacture it."

The situation placed Sarah in a dilemma. She had worked hard to obtain needlework for the seamen's wives in Boston. She knew that sewing was probably the most attractive work by which women could earn a living, and it was far from her wish to destroy this source of income. At the same time she knew how much work—how many hours of tedious, eye-straining effort—went into the elaborate costumes of the day. Yards and yards of material had to be hemmed and tucked; ruffles gathered and carefully sewed on; braiding in intricate designs to be added—all by tiny stitches made by hand. And for scanty pay. Sarah pondered: Would it be possible to manufacture a sewing machine for home use only? It would be a great boon to the mother who could not afford a seamstress.

Sarah had learned that a frontal attack often boomeranged, whereas a flanking maneuver could be much more effective. So she began a series of articles on the hard lot of the seamstress—the many hours of labor she must put into a gown for some wealthy woman, a gown the maker herself could never hope to wear. The exhausting effort of sitting all day bent over her sewing, the eye strain, the meager pay, were stressed until Sarah's readers—the women of the nation—were gently nudged into a frame of mind that would accept, even demand, a sewing machine. And, as Sarah well knew, when the women demanded something, it would be done.

One summer morning Sarah came downstairs to find the house, as usual on Mondays, filled with steam and the smell of soap. She paused in the doorway of the kitchen, where a huge copper boiler took up a large share of the stove. The weekly washerwoman had come early to get the work done before the heat of the day. She was bent over a wooden washboard, her body moving back and forth rhythmically as she scrubbed the clothes on the corrugated surface. Sweat streamed down her face; her hair hung in limp wisps along her neck.

The sight depressed Sarah. She had always hated Monday with its smell of wetness and yellow soap, but in summer it was particularly hateful. Something should be done about it. All the way down Chestnut Street the horses' hoofs seemed to beat out the words of the "Washing Day Song," which everyone in Philadelphia was singing:

> *"With her sleeves rolled to the elbow,*
> *And her arms deep in the suds,*
> *She is scrubbing and rubbing,*
> *Rubbing and scrubbing—*
> *To clean her rich mistress's duds!"*

"I must do something about eliminating washings by hand," Sarah muttered as she went up the wooden stairs to her office. She sat at her desk, her quill pen poised above the paper for a moment, and then wrote:

Will not some man of inventive genius turn his mind to the solving of the problem of washing day? We shall be pleased to give accurate accounts of any such projects, and, after viewing them, to tell our readers what promise they hold for lightening the awful burden that now makes this task almost unbearable.

Later she was able to announce that such a machine had been invented, and she published a picture of the new contraption. It was a barrel-like affair, turned with a hand crank to churn the clothes to cleanliness. Turning the crank was hard work, but not so hard as scrubbing on a washboard. Moreover, the operator could sit down at the task. Sarah advised her readers that the sum of forty dollars was not too much to pay for a device that would eliminate so much backbreaking work.

So far so good! Godey's *Lady's Book* circulation reached and passed forty thousand. But Graham's magazine was close behind.

Godey couldn't understand it. "You said, my dear, that there are more women than critics. Then where is Rex getting all those subscribers?"

Sarah smiled. "I suppose we should be glad to know that more and more people are becoming really educated. I have battled all my life for better instruction in the public schools and for higher education for women. Now we see the results. Why, sir, there must be more than one hundred thousand families reading magazines. Ours and Graham's and *The Saturday Evening Post, The North American Review,* and others. Isn't it wonderful, sir?"

"We can't let Rex Graham get ahead of us. Think of something, my dear. Something that Rex Graham can't copy!"

Sarah did think, but everything she started in the *Lady's Book* could be and was imitated in the *Gentleman's Mag-*

azine. Oh, for something, anything, that could be Godey's alone!

Then one day Sarah had a revolutionary idea. She had been publishing fashion plates for years, even though she disliked that part of her work. But all the fashions had been of dresses, cloaks, bonnets, and other outer wear. Never a word about the things that went underneath. Sarah couldn't restrain a chuckle. If she could start describing women's underclothes, that would set Graham back on his heels. He wouldn't dare attempt anything like that. If only she dared picture them! But that would be carrying things too far—that would shock her readers. No, she must content herself with describing dainty yet sensible underwear for women.

But what could she call these garments? "Underwear" was too crude; the popular term, "unmentionables," was too coy. No, she must find a word—something as effective and as popular as her "Domestic Science" had proved to be. She went on about her work, but the thought nagged at her mind.

A day or two later when she was reading over a list of imports from France, the word leaped out at her: "Lingerie"!

She repeated the word, "lingerie." "That means linen things—all sorts of linen things, of course. But we could use it to mean the linen garments worn under outer clothing— petticoats, stomachers, everything. I'll use it to mean all undergarments—whether of linen or silk or cotton or wool. It sounds like the perfect word!"

And so she wrote:

> Good taste demands that a lady's *lingerie* shall be as dainty, yet simple, as her purse permits. Frenchwomen spend a great deal of time and effort in fashioning lace and embroidery to trim these garments, which, though they never meet the eye of the observer, still speak silently of a lady's care in her toilet.

When Godey read this he gasped, then roared with laughter, slapping his thigh with his palm. "That will do it, my dear. How! Old Rex won't dare discuss *lingerie*, I'll wager!"

When that issue of the *Book* appeared in the sedate parlors of her subscribers, the reaction was more violent than Sarah had anticipated. Letters poured in upon her desk. They were about equally divided in praise and condemnation. Praise for her honesty in helping her readers to know what was right in this hitherto-neglected realm of fashion. Condemnation of her brashness in discussing such intimate apparel. But the word Sarah had chosen stuck, and gradually she saw it incorporated into the language.

These skirmishes for popularity between Graham and Godey were but minor affairs compared to the great battle of the engravings, or the Wooden Block Controversy, which soon engrossed the two publishers, their editors, and their subscribers.

Sarah had innocently remarked one day that Mr. Poe had mentioned that he favored simple woodcuts as illustrations for his magazine. He felt that they were in better taste than more elaborate illustrations, and he wanted them done by the finest artists.

Sarah knew, but did not point out, that the remark had been caused by some of the overelaborate "embellishments" Godey loved to use in his *Book*.

Godey himself was using woodcuts; they were cheap, quickly prepared, and so far had been satisfactory. But if Poe preferred woodcuts, Godey would look for something better.

One day he brought in to Sarah's office two fashion plates and laid them before her on her desk.

"Which is better, my dear?" he asked.

Sarah needed only one glance. "Why, this one, of course."
She indicated her choice. "It is far the better of the two."

Godey was delighted. "I knew you would say that. That
plate is made by the new steel-engraving process. Observe it
closely. Notice how fine the lines are, how exquisite the
shading! Well, what do you think? I am going to use steel
engravings for my fashion plates. That will show the world
who is leading in giving his readers the very latest innovations. How!"

Sarah agreed. "It will be a big step forward, sir. But aren't
such plates terribly expensive?"

Godey chuckled. "One steel engraving costs as much as
forty woodcuts. Or more. This woodcut cost me twenty
dollars; this steel engraving, eight hundred and forty dollars.
But I can afford at least one each issue—nothing is too good
for our fashions, my dear! Why, the whole country follows
the *Lady's Book* styles, and women have never been dressed
so beautifully and so elegantly."

Sarah knew this was true. By careful selection she had
gradually made the fashion plates of Godey's *Book* the ideal
of dress for every woman from the Atlantic seaboard to the
frontier. They could not all have such fashions, of course; but
they did their best. And as Sarah constantly reminded them,
it was not necessary to copy a fashion. Let it be a guide and
adapt it to one's particular purse and personality.

Godey went on thoughtfully, "I'd like to use these steel
engravings for my historical and scenic embellishments.
However, I'm not going to let the cat out of the bag too soon.
I want to spring this as a pleasant surprise on my readers—
and on Rex Graham!"

The steel engravings caused as great a stir as Godey
could hope for. Letters poured in from all parts of the
country, letters wild with praise for the innovation. Rival

papers leaped to criticize, saying that this was a useless extravagance; that Godey could spend his money to better advantage than in such foolishness.

Godey took the question straight to his readers, asking them to express their honest opinions of whether the engravings were worth their cost. The replies left no doubt in his mind.

Sarah took no part in the public debate, but the publisher devoted several pages in each issue to reviewing the situation and publishing letters. He chose, of course, only those that supported his side.

"In the great controversy regarding the Fashion Plates, we wish to say the ladies are unanimously in favor of the engravings and abominate the woodcuts," wrote the editor of the Long Island *Journal*.

"The fashion plates of this magazine are decidedly superior to those of competitors in beauty, correctness and value," was the verdict of the Ohio *Republican*.

Godey was jubilant over a letter from Pulaski, New York: "The Ladies' Fashion Plate matter cannot be decided by the ladies of our village, as the *Lady's Book* is the only magazine taken."

Bolstered by such enthusiastic praise, Godey went about beaming on everyone—but not for long. One day Godey heard the rumor that Poe had signed up the English engraver, John Sartain, to work for Graham's exclusively. The news shattered Godey's happiness.

"What right has Rex Graham to make such a contract?" he stormed, pacing back and forth in front of Sarah's desk. "It's infamous, that's what it is! Here I started using engravings, and I used Sartain's too—some of the time. He's undoubtedly the best for fine work. And now, behind my back——"

Sarah's clear laugh rang out. "Oh sir!" she said, her eyes twinkling with merriment. "Did you not clap your hands in approval when I signed N. P. Willis to write for us alone? Mr. Poe has just taken a leaf from your book——"

"Authors! What difference does that make? There are plenty to replace any that are under an exclusive contract. But good engravers are not so plentiful. You didn't see me making such a fuss when Poe paid Longfellow fifty dollars for a poem, even though I knew it was extravagant."

Sarah smiled reminiscently. "Yes, we have been able to get poems from Mr. Longfellow, Mr. Holmes, and others for twenty-five dollars. Only Mr. Lowell made us pay thirty."

"And when Rex paid Fenimore Cooper eighteen hundred dollars for that story, 'The Islets of the Gulf,' I just thought he was crazy. It didn't matter. But this is different. How!"

"Don't worry, sir," Sarah said soothingly. "Mr. Graham himself told me that that eighteen hundred dollars was poorly spent. The story did not bring in one new subscriber."

"But Sartain's engravings will bring in subscribers! I must find something to outshine them."

What the publisher found made Sarah shudder with distaste. It was a method of reproducing sketches by transfer of the design from the original by use of a special ink. It was called decalcomania, and for a short while Godey was so lavish in this type of illustration that some of his rivals nicknamed him the decalcomaniac.

Sarah, who was able to observe Godey's wild experiments with a detached air, saw clearly, as he did not seem to, that Godey's *Lady's Book* had but one purpose: not to outshine Graham's, but simply to carry into the homes all over the country news of the world, reports of women's progress in their uphill struggle for recognition, helps in their household work, and a little happiness, through stories and poems that would lift them out of their often dull surroundings and give them a taste of romantic life.

It was a large enough order, but not too large for Sarah's intuitive knowledge of what the American woman, who was just now emerging from her traditional cocoon, wanted. Sarah felt that it was her destiny to keep all women alerted to the scarcely noticeable movement. This she was doing, with her editorials, her own articles, and the articles and stories she chose to publish. And the women of America, like those of Pulaski, responded: In many a village across the continent the *Lady's Book* was the only magazine taken.

After some eighteen months as editor, Poe was dismissed from Graham's. He had brought the magazine from six thousand circulation to forty thousand. For a while it continued to worry Godey, but then its popularity began to decrease, and the *Lady's Book* was unconditionally the victor.

PROJECTS GALORE

"THE BATTLE OF THE GIANTS," IMPORTANT AS IT WAS IN Sarah's career, did not consume all her time and attention. Just as she assumed her place in the publishing world, taking up her duties, meeting her problems, so did she step into the social and civic life of the busy and progressive city. And just as she had become a force to be conjured with in the journalistic community, she made her influence felt in other areas of activity. Sarah soon saw that Philadelphia needed awakening to some of the same civic ills that plagued Boston.

Here, as in the Massachusetts city, the schools were almost wholly taught by men; children were brutally punished by both teachers and parents for even minor infringements of rules; and in the mills and factories now beginning to dot the Pennsylvania landscape, children were employed for long hours at exhausting work and for starvation wages. Here was a subject for Sarah's pen, and she turned out many editorials dealing with these abuses.

But she did not confine her interest to editorials. She visited the schools and observed at first hand the methods of teaching and of punishment. She became a familiar figure in the factories and let it be known that she was shocked at this new system of producing textiles and iron goods. She had deplored the old style of manufacturing, where each workman made an entire item, because under that system the owner of the manufactory could employ his help for as long hours and at as low wages as he wished.

The new system, only recently introduced, had still worse drawbacks. For the owner could still keep his workers on the job from daylight till dark, and after, and there was also the tedium of performing only one little part of the total operation.

In Boston she had learned of conditions in Shanty Town by visiting the area and talking to the people; now she began studying the actual situation in the mills springing up in the Kensington and Frankford sections. Here, for years, the textiles had been woven by Irish weavers, who did the work by hand. Now that the new system was being established, factories were springing up in the same districts, and with the factories the special type of tenement, the "bandbox" houses, peculiar to the Quaker City.

When Sarah visited such a factory and saw frail women and small children bent over spinning machines and looms, breathing lint-filled air, she wished she could dip her pen in fire to make the nation realize the evils of the system.

Traditionally, the working day was from sunup to sundown, no matter how many hours that encompassed. Almost half a century before Sarah came to Philadelphia, the carpenters of that city had begun to agitate against this and to demand shorter hours. At the time Sarah took over the editorship of the *Book*, the demand for a ten-hour day was stirring up the workers of the country—the men workers. Women and children were not included in the movement. They could work from sunup to sundown and far into the night if their employer wished to keep them that long. If they didn't like the hours, they could go home and starve.

This was worse than anything Sarah had known in her quiet farm home in New Hampshire. She knew it was wrong. One look at the faces, the gaunt forms of the textile workers, should be enough to convince anyone. But people weren't looking. Sarah tried to open their eyes by her editorials.

Then there was the housing problem. Philadelphia was noted for its sturdy, good-looking brick homes, but the city was crowded. Rooms were at a premium, and owners could charge whatever they wished for even the meanest shelter. And with the introduction of the factories, slums had arisen to house the workers who could pay only the minimum rent. Shocked at what she saw on her frequent pilgrimages through the city, Sarah began to write editorials pointing out the disadvantages to the city of having such ugly sections. She campaigned vigorously against high rents for the working people.

From such editorials it was but a step to appeal to the nation as a whole to combat the creeping cancer of slum areas. And then, one more step to the very revolutionary idea that every American family, in city or country, should own its home. With a feeling of exhilaration, Sarah suggested the motto, "Own Your Own Home."

The idea struck an answering chord in Godey's heart. It was a splendid project. And he could help it along.

He came to Sarah's desk with the proof sheet of a new department. "I had it set up in type, my dear, so you could see how attractive it is. But, of course, you are to handle it, as you do everything but my own 'Arm Chair.'" He smiled down at the editor. "I have to fight to keep that, don't I?"

Sarah picked up the sheet the publisher laid before her.

Across the top in the fancy lettering Godey loved was the title: GODEY'S MODEL COTTAGES. Below this was the engraving of the first "model cottage." Sarah looked at it and felt a shiver of distaste through her whole body.

"Oh sir!" she gasped. "Not that!"

Godey looked hurt. "And why not, my dear? I think it is eminently practical for a country cottage. And the engraving is exquisite."

Sarah's shock gave way to merriment, and she tried in vain to suppress the giggles that shook her. Glancing at the sketch again, she began to read the description: *A Swiss-German model.* The engraving showed a cottage with thatched roof; the woodwork around doors and windows was carved into fantastic shapes. A cowshed was joined to the parlor. There was no barn, and Sarah wondered what would happen in a cold New England winter. Would the cow be brought into the parlor to keep warm? The shed would not do.

She glanced up, her eyes twinkling, but when she saw Godey's unhappy expression, she tried to look serious.

"I don't think this is quite suitable for America, sir," she said gently.

"And why not, my dear?"

A reminiscent look came into Sarah's eyes. "I was thinking of my father's farmhouse—a story-and-a-half building, very plain and simple and dignified and—" she hesitated for a moment "—and lovely. New England homes, sir, were not overdecorated like this. And as for thatched roofs—where can they be found in this country?"

Godey took the sheet from Sarah's hand and studied it, frowning. "I think it's very attractive. I admire your passion for simplicity, my dear, but there is room for elegance also. Here in America, we need more elegance—in farmhouses as well as city mansions. Of course," he conceded slowly, "this is just a beginning. The plans will improve with time and experience."

Sarah sighed and said no more. It was the same old controversy—the one point on which she differed with her employer. She had a passion for simplicity and he had an equally strong attachment to elaborateness. And he owned the *Book*. As with the fashion plates, she would have to give in. Perhaps in time she could somewhat modify his choice of "model cottages."

It wasn't going to be easy, she knew, and in the years that followed, Sarah almost gave up hope. It seemed that again Godey had hit on something that delighted his readers, and "*Lady's Book* houses" began to spring up across the country from Philadelphia to the West.

The difference in personality between Sarah and her publisher was so marked that those who knew them often wondered how they "hit it off so well." The fact was that the two made an excellent team. The country was just emerging from its first period of hardship and privation that goes with any new settlement. The women were craving for elegance and richness in their surroundings. Their husbands were prosperous and could afford some furbelows. Godey gave them elegance and furbelows with a vengeance, and they blessed him for it. At the same time some economy and thrift were still necessary, and the teachings and habits of earlier years could not be entirely discarded. Sarah catered to this innate need.

Godey, recognizing and admiring Sarah's talent, usually gave her almost free rein. Sarah recognized Godey's ability as a publisher—ability that had won him the title "Prince of Publishers." She could not help seeing how avidly the women of the country consumed every detail of the ornate fashions and impossible houses. So, though she occasionally tried to tone down Godey's exuberance, she knew that it was partly due to that very lack of taste that the *Book* was the most widely read journal in the country and was fast approaching the day when it could claim the largest circulation of any magazine in the whole world.

Godey never interfered with Sarah's campaigns for the betterment of the status of women. He had placed only two limitations upon her work: religion and politics must never be mentioned.

Sarah was free to rejoice in the activities of Queen Victoria, declaring that there would certainly be a change in the way of life of the English people. They had had "pernicious examples," Sarah declared, in the sons of George III, but the present sovereign was setting a far different example.

"The hereditary sovereign of England has very little real power in the government," she pointed out, "but on manners and morals his or her example acts with tremendous effect." Then she went on to predict that the queen "may so stamp her influence on the period that history will speak of it as her own. It will be the Victorian, as the former one is now the Elizabethan."

She was free to write columns praising Florence Nightingale and urging that schools for nurses be established in this country. The experiences of the English girl should prove an object lesson to the Americans.

Florence Nightingale gave Sarah a living example to point up her long campaign for women nurses and physicians. And now she was given an example right here at home. A young woman, Elizabeth Blackwell, wanted to be a doctor and had been refused admittance to any of the medical colleges. Most newspapers and magazines had no sympathy for the girl, saying that she was either wanton or crazy. But Sarah took up the fight, writing blazing articles about the narrow-mindedness that kept women from this field.

"Many women feel that it is immodest to employ a male physician," she declared, "but they are denied the privilege of having a woman attend them. Is this fair or equable?" She asked if men were afraid to compete with women doctors, and suggested, "If they cannot cope with women in the medical profession, let them take an humble occupation in which they can."

It was largely Sarah's championship that won the battle, and Elizabeth Blackwell was finally admitted to the Geneva Medical School in western New York State. Sarah kept watch on her progress, and when she was graduated, Sarah triumphantly hailed her as the first woman in America to win the degree of Doctor of Medicine.

Sarah's interest in medical affairs did not stop there. Besides urging that women be trained as doctors and nurses to serve in this country, she advocated that female medical missionaries be sent to backward countries and to India where the social system posed a serious threat to adequate care of women patients. It required many years of hammering away at this idea before a small breach was made in the wall of prejudice. Sarah had been writing for Godey's magazine for more than thirty years when, in 1869, a Miss Swain was sent out, "the first lady with a full medical diploma to go out in a missionary capacity to the women of the East."

The question of the property rights of women was another problem that attracted Sarah's attention. She had been shocked when the meager wages of one of the women in the Seaman's Aid Society had been seized to pay her husband's debts. Sarah had learned, then, that it made no difference that the woman earned the money and needed it to feed her family—the money belonged to the husband. And everything the woman owned upon marriage became the husband's property. Sarah pointed out the unfairness of this situation and pled for a more just law.

Godey was constantly amazed at the amount of work his editress turned out. She not only edited the *Book*, reading manuscripts, meeting authors and illustrators, proofreading, discussing make-up. She also reviewed dozens of books in every issue, and reviewed them only after reading them. In this capacity Sarah was usually generous in her comments; but when something struck her as really bad, she did not hesitate to say so. She was appalled at Ned Buntline's *Mysteries and Miseries of New York* and exclaimed, "Horrible! The details are shocking and revolting!"

In addition to this work for the *Book*, she compiled a yearly anthology, the de luxe gift of the time; edited cookbooks, books on manners and social usage; edited books for Harper's and several other publishing houses; and she was continuously working on a book of her own.

Godey loved to compare his paragon with the editors of rival magazines. There was the unpredictable Poe at Graham's. A story, maybe a poem, and some literary criticism were all that could be expected other than his regular editorial duties. And many other editors did not contribute even that much to their magazines. But Sarah, as Godey often remarked, was "truly a marvel. I'm the luckiest publisher in the country. How!"

Though the professional rivalry among the leading magazines, particularly between Graham's and Godey's, was strong and bitter, the personal relations were warm and friendly. Publishers, artists, and authors formed a convivial social circle that frequently met for pleasant dinners and conversation. Graham's home was often the scene of such gatherings.

The Graham home on Arch Street was a handsome one. It had a huge dining room centered with a large oval table. Above this hung a chandelier of bubble crystals, which reflected the light of dozens of candles. These reflections were repeated and multiplied by mirrors around the walls, so that the company seemed many times larger than it really was.

Mr. and Mrs. Graham presided over the huge, heavily laden table with lavish hand. Their guests would almost certainly include the most important figures along Publishers' Row: Louis Godey, the Peterson brothers, Rufus Griswold; such artists as Thomas Sully, John Sartain, and Felix Darley; editors such as Poe and Sarah; and writers— those who lived in Philadelphia like Grace Greenwood and Eliza Leslie, and any visiting celebrities.

Naturally the men outnumbered the women five to one; but even without this advantage Sarah held her own in the brilliant company. The only concession in dress that she had made to time and to her improved financial status was one of quality. Her dresses were still simple and dignified but now she could afford the very finest silks; and the lace at throat and wrist and the small lace cap were the exquisite handiwork of French needlewomen. The fashion exactly suited her and at the same time set her apart from some of the other women guests at the literary gatherings and from such highly fashionable ladies as Mrs. Graham.

Seated at the Grahams' oval table, under the chandelier with its sparkling crystal pendants, Sarah would look across at her rival editor, Poe, and her heart would contract with pity for the pale man in his somber black suit and black stock knotted over snowy linen. Sarah knew that that linen might be frayed and worn, but it would be spotless.

She was well aware of Poe's poverty. Sometimes she was a guest in his little house, where his wife Virginia half reclined, pale and ill, in a big chair and his mother-in-law, Mrs. Clemm, bustled about to serve tea and small cakes. At other times she met Mrs. Clemm with her basket on her arm, returning from shopping for her two loved ones.

Sarah's eyes would stray from the poet's dark, intense face to the faces of the other guests, all so well fed and hearty, so full of life and plans. She felt at home among these notables of the journalistic world; she enjoyed being with them. She could "talk their language" with an authority they respected. She did not have to speak loudly; her low, cultivated voice attracted attention. And she could listen with a real interest that was flattering to any speaker. She knew that her employer was not only satisfied with her work; he was enthusiastic. Whenever his small blue eyes rested upon her, they reflected his approval; he always spoke to her with obvious deference and admiration. She could criticize him, as she sometimes did, suggesting that he tone down some jubilant article in praise of the *Book* or some extravagance in a fashion plate. He would take such criticism meekly, though he did not always act upon it. But no one could criticize Sarah.

Though Sarah was thoroughly enjoying her "place in the sun," she was lonely for her children. They were still scattered—Horatio had not returned with the Wilkes expedition, but had left it when it reached Oregon on its return trip. He was now making a solitary journey through the Far West, studying and recording the languages of the various Indian tribes. William was practicing law in Virginia, and the two girls were teaching. Frances Ann had a position in a girls' seminary in New Jersey; Josepha was teaching in Georgia.

If only they could all be in Philadelphia with her, Sarah thought, she would be content. But they were not here. So Sarah devoted her Sunday afternoons to writing long letters to them, and tried to bury her loneliness under more and more work.

HIGHLIGHTED YEARS

IT WAS INEVITABLE THAT CHARLES DICKENS, TOURING America in 1842, should make an effort to see "the female genius of Philadelphia." England had nothing like Sarah, though it did boast a number of women writers of real distinction. But a woman who could be a writer and editor, founder and director of worthy institutions, and campaigner for recognition of the rights of women and children—all wrapped up in one handsome and distinguished lady—that was something only Philadelphia could claim. And Sarah had a still firmer call on the British author's interest: She had never pirated any of his stories, as practically every other magazine in the country had done.

Pirating was a sore point with Dickens, who had come to America partly to look into the situation and to let Americans know how he felt. He found that his books were selling in tremendous quantities in this country, and he was getting not a penny from the sales. The profit was going entirely to the publishers. It was stealing—there was no other word for it.

England at this time had a large number of popular

writers. As soon as a book appeared by Dickens, Thackeray, Frances Burney, Maria Edgeworth, Captain Frederick Marryat or any other popular British writer, it was snapped up by American publishers and rushed through a cheap edition. Enterprising publishers had scouts in England, watching for new books to be sent across the Atlantic by the fastest ship. Since no royalty was paid the author, these publishers derived a huge profit from such ventures.

Magazines had long been guilty of the same practice. It was Sarah, as editor of the *Ladies' Magazine*, who had first denounced the custom and declared she would not follow it. Dickens, who had caused a small uproar in New York and Boston by his frank discussion of American piracy, must have been eager to see a woman who had stood firm in her resolve to pay for everything she published.

He came to Sarah's office frankly to observe the curious creature. He found her as elegant, courteous, and refined as any English lady, and as little perturbed by the visit of the great man as if such guests were everyday occurrences. She sat talking to the British "lion" perfectly at ease, her small white hands folded in her lap.

It was a new experience for the famous novelist, who had been so fawned over and kowtowed to with such adoration that it had bored him and made him contemptuous of the American public. He left the interview with a higher opinion of women in business—and of all American women—than he had gained from his reception in Boston and the great ball in his honor in New York.

Godey was delighted at this proof of the fame of his editress. After the Britisher had gone, the publisher burst into Sarah's office, his face alight.

"Do you know, my dear, that other editors have had to

seek out Mr. Dickens and beg for an interview. But you! You brought him here to Godey's *Book*. How! And what did you think of him?"

Sarah considered. "Well, I couldn't see much of his face because of his beard. It almost hid the diamond that held his bright green tie. It even almost covered his velvet vest with the gold watch chain and dangling charms." She shuddered delicately. "I do hope our American men do not take up that ugly fashion!"

"They have already done so! Haven't you noticed the new, unshaven appearance of the men we meet?"

"I'll fight it!" Sarah declared, remembering David's handsome, clean-shaven face. "I'll point out to the women how ridiculous men look with their faces hidden behind a thick, stiff brush!"

Godey grinned. "Well now, we have one more great patriotic cause to champion!"

Sarah's quick mind was already searching for the proper approach to this new campaign. She was serious, but if she showed this seriousness too plainly it would backfire. People would laugh at her . . . laugh? That might be the answer. Attack beards with humor, puns, epigrams that could be repeated with a chuckle. Sarah had seldom utilized humor in her writing, but now she was delighted with the possibilities of such a campaign. What should she call bearded men? Whiskerandos! The word came unbidden to her mind.

The next issue of the *Book* had several references to the new American—the Whiskerando. He was described as one who must be afraid to show his face, who must not be trustworthy, "for honesty and fair dealing have no motive for such concealment." If a man did not go in for whiskers but was content to wear only a mustache, he was said to have "caught the mustache rabies, and had a stiff little brush pasted under his nose."

Riddles were a popular feature of every magazine and newspaper, which used them to fill up every inch of space not otherwise employed. Often prizes were offered for correct answers to some of the more difficult conundrums. Sarah aimed her riddles at the new fashion.

"Why are men with beards and mustaches the most modest men in society?" she asked. And on another page gave the answer: "Because they are the least barefaced!"

Sarah had her weapon and her ammunition, but for a time her battle seemed only to increase the popularity of the facial adornment she disliked. Her sneering "Whiskerandos" was met by a proud "Boz Locks," in honor of Dickens. Her riddles were met by other riddles. One Philadelphia newspaper publisher, who had himself taken up the fashion, asked, "What is a kiss without a mustache like?" He printed the answer upside down, so there could be no cheating: "It is like an egg without salt!"

The battle became hilarious, and finally Sarah had to admit one of her few defeats. She was making little headway against beards, and there were graver problems to be met.

The year of Dickens' visit brought a real triumph to gladden Sarah. On the morning of July 23, 1842, the last stone was laid and the Bunker Hill Monument was finally complete. It stood 221 feet high, a granite shaft that had been seventeen years in the building and had cost more than one hundred and fifty thousand dollars. Sarah read the glowing stories and smiled. The women of the country had supplied a goodly portion of that money—and not only the money but the determination that the monument should not be abandoned.

Though the monument was finished, the committee decided to postpone the dedication until the anniversary of the battle, on June 17 of the coming year.

Sarah would have loved to attend the ceremony—to hear the speeches, see old friends, and, unquestionably, be awarded a portion of the praise that would be showered upon all who had worked to make the monument a fact. But it was a long trip from Philadelphia to Boston, and she did not feel that she could undertake it. She had never liked to travel and had done as little as possible.

She realized that times had changed radically even in the few years she had been in Philadelphia. The new trains were traveling at twenty miles an hour, "annihilating space and time!" she declared in an article. She would have liked to hear Senator Daniel Webster's dedication speech, and to chat with him afterward, reminiscing about their earlier efforts concerning the monument. But it was too far to travel, even for such satisfactions.

Sarah had another reason for not wishing to leave Philadelphia, even for a few weeks. For the first time in years most of her family were near her. She was basking in the happiness of seeing them daily, hearing accounts of their activities, and watching with pride the honors bestowed upon them.

Horatio had at last returned from his wanderings and had married and settled down in Philadelphia. His report to the government on the languages of the Indians of the West had earned him a reputation as the most eminent philologist in the country. He had an excellent government position, and his report was published and quoted. Sarah was very proud of Horatio's achievement.

William, too, was married and practicing law in Virginia. He was not too far away to make regular visits to the Quaker City. Josepha was making plans to open a school for older girls in Philadelphia. She had hoped to have her sister, Frances Ann, as a partner in the venture, but Fanny had other plans. She had met a young naval surgeon, Dr. Lewis Boudinot Hunter, and after a quiet courtship their engagement had been announced.

So Sarah gave up all ideas of attending the Bunker Hill Monument dedication without regret. She read all the accounts, imagined all the noise and excitement, and felt she was there in spirit, at any rate.

A few days after the dedication Sarah found on her desk a small package, sent to her from a friend in Boston. Opening it with curiosity, she found a small glass cup plate. It was an unusual gift, and Sarah picked it up to examine it more closely. A delighted smile erased the questioning look from her face. She rose swiftly and rustled into Godey's office.

"Look, sir!" she cried. "This is really a compliment! A triumph!"

The publisher took the tiny object in his plump hands and turned it this way and that. Then he, too, smiled delightedly.

"It is no more than you deserve, my dear . . ." He paused suddenly and frowned. "It is not as much as you deserve!" he corrected himself. "Your name should be here."

Sarah retrieved the cup plate, smiling tenderly at it. "Oh no, sir! This is enough! To think that Mr. Deming Jarves considered our part worthy of memorializing in this fashion! I love the motto!" She held the small glass up to the light and examined the workmanship. There on the miniature saucer was impressed a replica of the Bunker Hill Monument. Above it were the words: STARTED BY THE MEN, 1825 and below the phrase that had pleased Sarah so much: FINISHED BY THE LADIES, 1842.

"I wonder whether Mr. Jarves' Sandwich glassworks turned out other souvenir pieces," she said meditatively. "I wouldn't mind having a water pitcher for my room. It would be a happy reminder of a long, hard struggle."

Godey nodded. "We'll see, my dear. I am glad that even this recognition has been made—the speakers said little enough about it!" He sounded cross.

"Oh well," Sarah shrugged. "We are used to that, sir."

She returned to her office, cradling the little souvenir in her hands. It was silly, she thought, to be so pleased over such a slight honor, but she couldn't help it.

The wedding of Frances Ann and Dr. Hunter was to take place at Horatio's lovely home, where the family gathered to share the happy event. Not only were all of Sarah's children present—the boys with wives and children—but her beloved brother Horatio had taken a vacation from his law office in Glens Falls, New York. He was visiting his sister with his whole family, and they found much to talk about. Sarah was poignantly reminded of her own wedding day thirty-one years ago.

On the evening before the wedding, they all assembled in Horatio's parlor.

"It's like old times!" William exclaimed. "Come, Mother, play for us and let's sing our old favorites."

Sarah needed no persuading. She went to the small Mozart piano that was Horatio's pride, and began to play. They started with John Howard Payne's well-loved "Home, Sweet Home," which they had sung ever since it swept the country in the early 'twenties.

Then, " 'The Watcher! The Watcher!' " William demanded. "Your song is sung everywhere, Mother. I predict that it will be as lasting a favorite as Payne's."

Horatio Buell smiled fondly at his sister. "Yes. We know it too. Everyone is singing it."

Sarah's slender fingers moved over the keys as she played the first high, sweet notes of the new popular melody, and the little group around the piano raised their voices in song:

> *"The night was dark and fearful,*
> *The blast went wailing by—*
> *A Watcher, pale and tearful,*
> *Looked forth with anxious eye.*
> *How wistfully she gazes—*
> *No gleam of morn is there!*
> *And then her heart upraises*
> *Its agony of prayer!"*

As one, they sang the verses that told the tragic story of a poverty-stricken mother, watching her sick child die.

For a moment after the song ended there was silence in the room. Then Josepha suggested, "Play my favorite, Mother!" The spell was broken as they joined gaily in their childhood rhyme, "Mary Had a Little Lamb."

Sarah's heart was filled with love and pride. How fortunate she had been, after all! And how she wished David—both Davids—could be with them tonight. Her husband would surely be satisfied with the way she had brought up their children.

She recalled how her Newport neighbors had kindly offered to take in the children so that she, the young widow, could go into domestic service. She had had the courage to stand alone, and because of this the door had been opened to many other mothers so that they could earn a living and at the same time keep their children beside them.

But if Sarah was proud of her children, they were prouder still of their famous mother. Her life had been busy and full and she had accomplished much; yet even now, in 1844, at the age of fifty-six, she showed no sign of letting up or resting on her laurels. Later that evening, after Sarah had gone to bed, William remarked upon her vigor and enthusiasm.

"She has always been one step ahead of the crowd," he declared. "I wonder what her next project will be."

"Not just *one*, Will. Mother never has less than a dozen campaigns in mind. She is eager to have women sent as missionaries to India—especially if they are trained as doctors too. Medical missionaries, Mother calls them. And then she is campaigning for women teachers to be sent to the frontier. The children out in the West should not be neglected, and women could do the job better than men. Anyway, Mother contends that men can serve their country best by carrying on exploration and such things that women can't do," Josepha added.

William nodded. He knew that his mother had read with great interest a copy of John Charles Frémont's first published report on his exploration of the West. She was firmly convinced that the "manifold destiny" of the country lay in expansion of the West, as Frémont and other statesmen believed.

Sarah had not openly advocated expansion, for the one stipulation Godey had insisted upon was that the *Lady's Book* should have nothing to do with politics or religion. But through her championship of women teachers for the frontier, she was indirectly approving of the Westward movement.

"Mother is working hard to get more normal schools established for women—" Josepha went on.

William interrupted with a chuckle, "That's not a new

campaign, Josie! Why, remember how thrilled and excited Mother was when the first normal school was opened in Lexington, Massachusetts, five years ago?"

"She had a right to be proud. Because of her editorials in the *Ladies Magazine*, that first normal school was for *women*. The second was for men teachers. It was the first time anything at all had been started for women before the men had a chance at it."

Josepha went on to mention other projects in which her mother was involved: the lowering of tenement rents, home ownership, more comfortable dwellings, women in the nursing and medical professions, the abolishment of corporal punishment in the schools, free playgrounds for children.

"And, Will, have you seen her new series of articles on physical exercise for girls and women? Goodness, are they starting something! Every month she shows some 'gentler sort of gymnastics suited to girls.' She started out with gentle exercises all right—just waving a scepter about. But you should see what she is advocating now. It would make Amazons of us all!"

She picked up the latest issue of the *Book* and turned the pages. She paused, smiling, and held it out to her brother. He looked at the pictures and grinned with appreciation of his sister's comment. It showed a series of exercises on a trapeze bar, with an attractive girl swinging herself about with ease and grace.

"I guess it won't hurt today's girls," Will observed. "They're getting used to all sorts of activity."

"Thanks to Mother!" Josepha retorted. "She is encouraging us to get out-of-doors more. Her articles on equestrianism, illustrated with engravings, have made quite a stir. And now it's picnics!"

Will raised his eyebrows. "Picnics?"

"Yes. Pack up a tasty lunch, she says, and take it out into the country. Eat it underneath the trees, by a sparkling brook if possible. She suggests Laurel Hill or some pretty grove on the Wissahickon. And the idea is becoming very popular. Almost any afternoon this summer the most elegant ladies and gentlemen can be seen boating on the river or chatting under the trees—and always with well-filled lunch baskets."

"I suppose it's the lunch baskets that attract the gentlemen."

"That's the purpose of them, Will. Why, Mother even quite openly hints that a few picnics might easily pay off with a proposal of marriage. It is her way of tempting the women to get outside in the sunshine and fresh air. And it gets results. How! as our Mr. Godey would say."

The wedding the next day was one of the happiest events in Sarah's life as she watched her elder daughter, beautiful and accomplished, give her hand in marriage to a handsome and successful young man. This marriage meant an end to her own years of loneliness, for Frances had made her mother promise to move into the Hunters' attractive new home, where a room had been furnished especially for her.

It was a lovely, bright room, furnished exactly to Sarah's taste. Four long windows were curtained in gleaming white, and in each hung a wicker cage holding her pet birds. The little feathered creatures had filled Sarah's many lonely evenings with song, and she could not bear to part with them now. A comfortable low rocker sat in front of the fire-place; in the center of the large room was a table-desk, holding her inkpot and quill pens, her lamp, and her ever-present bowl of grapes. The large bed was half hidden in a wide alcove. The walls were lined from floor to ceiling with shelves holding the hundreds of books that Sarah received for review. One special case held Sarah's own books, with the first slim volume of poetry leading an array that included different editions of *Northwood* and *Flora's Interpreter*, *Liberia*, cookbooks, books on etiquette, her anthology of poetry, her dictionary of poetical quotations and translations of her works into French, German and Italian.

To this room Sarah could retreat after a strenuous day in the office and spend her evening hours reading or writing some of the hundreds of letters she sent out concerning one or another of her pet undertakings.

She was also hard at work on her great project, *Woman's Record*, a complete history of woman's progress through the ages. She planned to use the biographies of all the women who had won recognition in any field, and in any land or age. The book was to be divided into four eras, the first era covering forty centuries from the creation to the birth of Christ, the last era discussing contemporary women.

To collect all this material, obtain engravings of the women's portraits, and write in longhand the series of more than two thousand biographies, was taking years of painstaking effort. The correspondence involved was in itself a tremendous amount of work. So Sarah was glad to have this spacious, comfortable room where she could work uninterruptedly.

The twentieth anniversary of the *Lady's Book* was approaching in 1850, and Louis Godey began making elaborate plans for a special edition. The *Book* was now being sent to every state in the Union and to every Territory; its circulation had multiplied steadily since Sarah's advent; it was time to celebrate.

"One thing I must have, my dear, is a portrait of my editress. Our readers have long been asking for this favor. It will be our present to them on our anniversary."

Sarah, no longer able to deny the request, consented to sit for a portrait.

Godey, delighted that Sarah had at last bowed to the wishes of her publisher and her public, gave the commission for the portrait to W. B. Chambers, one of the foremost artists in the city. Chambers was charmed with his subject. Sarah, at sixty-one, was still lovely to look at: her face remained unlined, her complexion fresh, her eyes bright and keen, her hair untouched by gray. But what most pleased the artist's eye was Sarah's charmingly simple manner of dress reminiscent of the 1820's. To artist Chambers, his model seemed ageless, unmarred by the passing years or the changing foibles of style.

Amused at the artist's enthusiasm, Sarah repeated some of his extravagant praise at home. Frances smiled. "I don't suppose you told him about the vinegar-and-brown-paper plasters?" she teased gently.

Sarah shook her head. "Of course not. That's my secret."

"Well, I won't tell either, Mother. You may apply your little plasters in perfect secrecy!"

Sarah did not mind this teasing. It was well known in the household that she kept in her top bureau drawer sheets of brown wrapping paper and a small bottle of apple vinegar. Each night before going to bed she applied strips of the paper soaked in vinegar to her forehead and temples—to keep away the crow's feet of age.

As for her clear complexion, Sarah attributed that and her general good health to the grapes she ate daily. Ever since that long-ago autumn on the hills with David, no matter how expensive or how difficult to obtain, Sarah always kept grapes in her room—not to much for her health, perhaps, but as a reminder of the husband she had lost.

Other artists now clamored to paint the well-known editress, and Sarah had to sit for Thomas Buchanan Read, whose poems she had often purchased for the *Book*, and for the daguerreotypists who were becoming so popular.

Both Sarah and Godey were justly proud of the anniversary edition. Sarah's portrait by Chambers appeared as the frontispiece, delighting the thousands of readers who had almost given up hope of ever seeing what their favorite editor looked like. Then, following a carefully selected group of stories and poems, the "Editor's Table" had good news to announce: The first female medical college had just been opened in Philadelphia, and the Female Medical Education Society of Massachusetts had been incorporated after a long and bitter fight with the state legislature.

A somber note was struck by Sarah's tender editorial on Edgar Allan Poe, who had died the previous October. But the sadness did not extend to Godey's "Arm Chair." The blithe spirit of the publisher was soaring: The *Book* had been increased by twelve pages, making a total of eighty-four. It was not only the largest magazine being published; it had the largest circulation. Godey wrote ecstatically: "Our edition is unprecedented in this or any other country; our model cottages are being reproduced all over the land; our advanced styles are worn in every city; and today's edition is nearly double that of any other magazine in the world!"

Reading the triumphant item, Sarah had not the heart to chide her employer for his jubilance. The *Book* was the largest and most popular journal in the world. The letters that flooded Sarah's desk from all parts of the nation and from many foreign countries showed that the readers gave Sarah the credit for this success. Godey himself gave his editor the credit. He brought the anniversary edition in and laid it on Sarah's desk. It was open to her portrait.

"The best investment I ever made, my dear," he said happily, "was purchasing the *American Ladies' Magazine*. I knew I was no editor myself—but I knew how to pick one. How!"

═══════○□○═══════ 14

THE WORLD SPEEDS UP

ONE OF THE MANY CONTRIBUTORS SARAH HAD INHERITED with her editorial job was Miss Eliza Leslie. This Philadelphia author, some twenty years younger than Sarah, had contributed to Godey's magazine since its earliest days, and continued to do so after Sarah took over the editorship.

Miss Leslie was one of the first Philadelphians to greet the newcomer, and the two women soon became good friends. The author's whole family was talented and wealthy, and it pleased Sarah to help promote the work of a woman who was not content to remain idle at home, enjoying the riches produced by others.

There was a still further bond between the two women: Miss Leslie was eager and energetic and not afraid to undertake new ventures. Sarah realized that in this friend she had a contributor who would go anywhere, even endure hardship, to obtain material for the *Book* she loved.

Sarah had for some time been toying with another revolutionary idea: She would like to send a woman to attend events of national importance and to write about them for the magazine's widely scattered readers. Back in the

1840's, while pondering the wisdom of trying out her scheme at the dedication of the Bunker Hill Monument, she had thought immediately of Miss Leslie. She was just the person to send. Unfortunately, at that precise time Miss Leslie had been herself editing a small monthly paper and could not leave on an assignment for Sarah.

Sarah sat at her desk and contemplated a world that seemed to be whirling around at an alarming rate. The marvelous magnetic telegraph had proved successful. Texas was admitted to the Union. Colonel John Frémont had traveled the great West back and forth and emigrants were flocking to Oregon. Steel rails were linking cities and hamlets across the country. The new factory system was flourishing and the nation was turning out miles of textiles, tons of iron products, acres of glass and pottery.

Sarah sighed. She could no longer keep in touch with everything while sitting behind an office desk. She needed eyes and ears in many places. Yet what could she do? In addition to the fact that she hated travel, she was too burdened with her regular work to make any excursions. She must send someone . . . and Eliza Leslie seemed the ideal choice.

Sarah tactfully broached the subject to her friend one day in the spring of 1845:

"I've been thinking, Eliza—one of the things that has hindered the advancement of women has been the way they have been isolated in their homes. They have not been able to get around to see and to learn what's going on. But now these new steam railroads will change that—or should change it. Don't you agree?"

Miss Leslie did agree. "Stage travel has been awkward and difficult and so expensive that few women could afford it. These new locomotives should be much more comfortable."

"Have you traveled by way of the steam railroad?" Sarah asked.

Eliza shook her head. "I hope to do so, though. Perhaps I shall have the opportunity this summer."

Sarah's smile lit up her face. "You shall, Eliza! If you wish it." With a rush of words, Sarah then unfolded her unique plan. The *Book* would pay all Miss Leslie's expenses if she would make the trip to Niagara Falls, keep a careful account of every penny it cost, record everything of interest, and write a series of articles for the *Book*.

"I selected Niagara Falls because so many people are discussing its wonders," Sarah explained.

Eliza's eyes glowed with enthusiasm. "It would be a thrilling experience. I'd love to undertake it."

"It might be dangerous," Sarah cautioned. "You'd be an unaccompanied woman, and a woman traveling alone may meet with unpleasant situations."

Eliza had no qualms. The trip appealed to her adventurous nature, and she was not unaccustomed to travel. Her father had taken his family to London and Portugal when Eliza was a mere child, and later Miss Leslie had visited her brother in England.

Careful plans and preparations were made, and when all was in readiness, Sarah told her readers what they could expect: an accurate, careful account of an unaccompanied lady's journey from Philadelphia to Niagara Falls and back:

> We calculate the distance at nearly 400 miles each way. Miss Leslie will travel the entire distance unaccompanied and she will tell our readers exactly what they may expect to find on such a journey. Whether it will be encouraging or not, we await Miss Leslie's report to decide.

One summer morning both Sarah and Godey were up bright and early to see Eliza off on the train to Perth Amboy which was to leave the depot at the Walnut Street wharf at 6:00 A.M. The train, as usual, was late, and they stood together, chatting excitedly while they waited. When the "All Aboard" was called, the three of them entered the coach and Mr. Godey checked to see that Eliza was comfortably seated.

At one end of the long car was a small room, and Godey indicated this with a wave of his hand.

"There's a ladies' car, Miss Leslie. You are fortunate." He escorted her to the door, but a large sign declared NO GENTLEMEN ADMITTED, so he bade her good-by and godspeed, and politely retired from the scene, to await Sarah outside.

Sarah anxiously regarded her friend. "Have you everything, Eliza? Do be careful. And—" a mischievous gleam twinkled in her eyes "—do keep notes! I want to know everything. Why, this may be the wedge that will open travel to thousands of women—women who have always been bound so closely to home that they have not known that anything existed outside their four walls."

Eliza sniffed. "I'm afraid that men are not going to like the idea. They've had the running to and fro pretty well to themselves so far. Stage travel never seemed to bother them or to keep them at home. Now we'll give their wives a chance, too, to see the world!"

"I hope so."

A great brass bell clanged, the engine sputtered and huffed, and a shower of smoke and cinders went sailing past the window. Sarah kissed Eliza gently on the cheek and turned from the room. She joined Godey on the platform and they watched the train chug and puff out of the station. "I am more excited than she is!" Sarah observed. "I do hope this proves to be a successful venture."

It did, as Godey's eager readers were to learn in subsequent issues of the *Book*, where the trip was reported in every minute and exciting detail.

At Perth Amboy, some forty miles from New York, Eliza left the steam cars and took the steamboat up to the New York wharf. The fare so far had been three dollars.

From New York she went up the Hudson to Albany by boat, with nothing to mar the smoothness of the journey. The female passengers were a bit jittery, of course, for it was almost customary for the steam boilers on trains and boats to explode. Every river in the country almost daily reported such accidents, many of which took a heavy toll of lives. And even though no serious accident occurred during Eliza's boat ride, the men on board took care to point out to the anxious women travelers the wreck of the steamboat *Swallow* as they passed. The gruesome details of the explosion in the night, the screaming passengers in the water, the death cries, were recounted with vividly graphic enthusiasm. As she listened, Eliza wondered whether all the men in the country had joined some silent brotherhood for the purpose of frightening women from the idea of traveling.

At Albany she again boarded a train, which sped over the ironshod, wooden rails at the terrific speed of twenty-one miles an hour. Once more she was fortunate to find a ladies' car. But at Utica, where the cars were switched, this luxury disappeared. When Eliza asked the conductor about this, he replied that "all cars were equally polite."

Eliza wasn't happy at the change, for she found herself in a crowded coach occupied mostly by bewhiskered men who smoked and spat with never-abating fervor. Most of them badly needed a bath—as yet Sarah's campaign for bathing at least once a week had not won many converts. Eliza consoled herself with the hope that the cars might again be changed before they reached Buffalo, and that they could then again "travel genteelly."

"It seems to be an ancient custom," she wrote later, "to put on the best vehicles at the beginning and end of the route, and the worst in the middle."

She found Buffalo a fine, young city. Though only thirty years old, it already gave promise of great industrial and social growth. The new town had been built on the site of the small village of wood cabins that was burned by the British in 1814.

Eliza Leslie, traveler that she was, was nevertheless totally unprepared for the sheer magnificence of the Falls themselves. In trying to describe them for her readers she called upon her extensive vocabulary of adjectives—most of them several syllables long. She palpitated with excitement as she wrote, and her readers responded with flutters of fascination and tremors of eagerness to see the marvelous sight, which was now being hailed as the Eighth Wonder of the World.

The entire trip, Eliza reported upon her return to Philadelphia, could be made in a week and should not cost more than fifty dollars for each person. Eager-eyed young ladies all across the country read the glowing description and made themselves a silent promise: They, too, would go to Niagara at the first opportunity. When, later, an enamored swain said, "Where shall we spend our honeymoon?" the answer was inevitable. Niagara Falls soon became the mecca of newly married couples. It owed much of its popularity to Eliza Leslie—and to Sarah, who had the idea of sending her there.

Godey's *Book* learned more from the trip than was visible in Miss Leslie's accounts. Sarah carefully studied her friend's voluminous and clear notes, from which she drew material for editorials and articles for months and years ahead. Some of the details that Eliza mentioned served later as springboards for campaigns for improvement in the railroads. The *Lady's Book* was to suggest that drinking water be supplied in the cars as a special consideration to women and mothers traveling with children. It would propose that sandwiches be sold at stations. Miss Leslie had been shocked at the way some passengers dillydallied over their meals when the train stopped at a station to allow travelers to go to the nearest hotel for breakfast, lunch, or dinner. Sandwiches would be convenient to serve many people and be less expensive, and might, perhaps, prevent the trains from being late due to the inconsiderate laggards.

The *Book* also advised that it would be a good idea to have each town's name clearly shown on the depot sign, and to have the conductor announce it a few miles before arriving. This would prevent the dismay and inconvenience experienced by so many who rode past their destination, unaware that they had reached it.

                        15

A SHRINE IS SAVED

SARAH HAD BEEN DEEPLY SHOCKED BY AN ARTICLE SENT TO her by Robert Criswell, Jr., concerning Mount Vernon, the home of George Washington. Mr. Criswell wrote that he had visited the place but had been refused admittance to the mansion, which was occupied by members of the John Augustine Washington family. He had wandered about the property, however, poking into brambles and trash heaps, and he had been disturbed by what he found.

"Everything about the grounds," he wrote, "seemed dilapidated and decaying, overgrown with briars, a scene of wreck and waste."

He went on to point out that Congress had been petitioned time and time again to purchase the property, but had done nothing. Now the present owners were willing to sell a hundred and fifty acres, including the mansion and tombs, for two hundred thousand dollars, but they would not sell to private enterprises. If the government would not take over the historic site, it would be permitted to go to utter waste.

An article of this nature was bound to arouse Sarah. She

had, she knew, saved the Bunker Hill Monument. Here was
an even more worthy cause. To her, George Washington
had always been a special hero; her whole childhood had
been spent in the glow of the country's adoration of the first
President. Only a baby in arms when he was elected, Sarah
had been eleven years old when he died. She could well remember the pall of mourning that enveloped the young
nation. She could recall, and always with emotion, sitting
beside her father during the solemn memorial service in the
Newport church. She could not understand how her countrymen could so far forget what Washington had done as to
permit his home to fall into ruin.

She laid aside Criswell's letter and began to write her
first editorial calling on the country to save Mount Vernon.
But after reading what she had written, she knew that it
would not do. Mount Vernon, of course, should be a shrine
for the entire nation. But it was in Virginia—in the South.
She was a Northerner, and Godey's *Book*, though it had
national circulation, was published in the North. She must
watch her words lest they be construed as a criticism of the
South for neglecting the historic home.

Sarah was keenly aware of the growing tension between
the two sections, of the bitterness stirred up by Harriet
Beecher Stowe's serial in the *National Era*. The story ran for
almost a year, with the North devouring every word about
Uncle Tom and Little Eva and Simon Legree and growing
more and more virulent over slavery, while the South was in
a rage over the distorted picture of life on the plantations.

Sarah slowly tore her editorial into bits and dropped them
into the wastebasket beside her desk.

"I can write letters," she murmured, "but I must wait for
a more favorable opportunity to come out publicly for the
preservation of Washington's home."

The more favorable opportunity came in 1856, when Miss Anne Pamela Cunningham, using the pseudonym, "A Southern Matron," founded the Mount Vernon Ladies' Association of the Union and began her campaign for funds with which to purchase and restore the estate.

Now that the project had been brought forward by a Southerner, Sarah felt that she could offer her assistance—but she must be diplomatic. She wrote to Miss Cunningham and deftly managed to get that ardent crusader to ask for help. Then she started her series of editorials and appeals:

> A novel plan has been formed for securing to the people of America the Home and Grave of the Father of our Country.
> Who that breathes the free air of our Republic does not feel that where Washington lived and died is the holiest spot in all our land? To make this spot the sacred inheritance of America's children to the end of time is the object now in view, and *woman* is the honored agent of the plan.

This was familiar ground. She had written similar appeals years ago in order to stir up women to contribute money for the completion of the Bunker Hill Monument.

Sarah went on to tell how the "Southern Matron" had tried to organize the women of the country; but without some way of reaching them, she had been handicapped. Now Godey's *Lady's Book* and the *Southern Literary Messenger* had come to her assistance. They would be the official organs —one in the North, the other in the South—to represent the Mount Vernon Ladies' Association and to collect funds.

Sarah asked every woman in the country to send in one dollar, which would make her a member of the patriotic group. They must obtain two hundred thousand dollars, but the women could raise that amount if they put their minds to it.

The women responded, as they always did to Sarah's

appeals. By October she could happily announce that some sixty thousand dollars had already been collected.

The following year she suggested that the Fourth of July be set aside as a national collection day. New York seized upon the idea and appointed Washington Irving as chairman. The famous lecturer, Edward Everett, with whom Sarah had worked on the Monument Fund, now offered to give a series of lectures on George Washington, donating the entire receipts to the Ladies' Association. The men who had let the idea of purchasing Mount Vernon languish were now enthusiastically following the women's lead.

Sarah encouraged women to contribute only money they had earned themselves. She suggested a novel method of raising funds—the rag fair, recently introduced in London. Remembering the success of the Monument Fair, Sarah explained that any small group could give a rag fair.

> Every attic, every work basket, every rag bag contains some good articles that are of no further use to the owners, but which someone else might find useful. Collect these items, clothing, dishes, books, utensils, or anything else of which you have grown weary. Display them in any hall, with the prices plainly shown. You may want to supplement the sale with cakes and bread from your own ovens, or preserves or pickles, or a supper. But if all the goods and all the work are given voluntarily, the receipts can be used for this patriotic purpose.

It was a novel idea . . . no one had ever held a rag fair in this country. Women took up the suggestion and rag fairs blossomed in almost every community.

Month by month the money poured in. There were the single dollar contributions; there was more than sixty-eight thousand dollars from Mr. Everett's lectures; there were the proceeds from the rag fairs and other money-raising projects. By March of 1860 the women of the country, with help from interested men, had collected the two hundred thousand dollars necessary, and Mount Vernon was purchased.

Sarah wrote victoriously:

> Mount Vernon now belongs to the American nation. Bought by the Ladies' Association of the Union, the last payment has been made. . . . We consider the complete success of the Mount Vernon Ladies' Association of the Union a great moral triumph because it bears the true stamp of patriotism and is the happy harbinger of faith in the permanence of our National Union.

"Oh," Sarah prayed softly as she finished her editorial, "that this may be the healing balm—that this may serve to soothe the wounded feelings of North and South and keep us one nation undivided!"

That was in March. In December of that same year South Carolina seceded from the Union.

16

A DAY OF THANKSGIVING

JUBILANT AS SHE WAS OVER THE SUCCESS OF THE MOUNT Vernon project, Sarah could not be entirely happy. With South Carolina's secession she realized that saving Mount Vernon had not saved the Union. By February of 1861 six other slave states had withdrawn from the Union, and by the time Abraham Lincoln was inaugurated President, the Secessionists had already named Jefferson Davis as President of the Confederate States of America.

To Sarah, love of the United States had all her life been a deep-seated passion. And because she loved the country—the whole country—she had been sensitive to the differences between the North and the South. She had felt, even back in 1827 when she wrote *Northwood*, that these differences need not separate the two sections. If only the people would try with love and generosity to understand each other, the dissimilarities could be made a bond rather than a matter for dissension.

Now, prevented by Godey's adamant rule that the *Lady's Book* should not mention politics or religion, Sarah could not openly voice her anguish at the declaration of war between the two segments of her beloved country. But maybe as an author she could do something.

She had already tried. When Mrs. Stowe's book had been stirring up the country, inflaming passions to the point of violence, Sarah had hoped that she might counteract the effect of the other woman's book by having her own *Northwood* republished. This had been the first novel ever to deal with slavery, but it had been written with sympathy for the South. And, while Sarah had not spent even one week in the South, which was all Mrs. Stowe had spent, she felt that her book presented a truer picture than the exaggerated one in *Uncle Tom's Cabin*, which appeared in book form in 1852.

The people were in no mood to read Sarah's gentle words. They were in no mood to listen when she said, "Differences cannot be settled by violence, as so many are suggesting. The great error of those people who would rather sever the Union than see a slave within its borders is that they forget that the master is their brother as well as the servant."

Northwood, which had been so well received in 1827, was now ignored. The book stood unnoticed on the dealers' shelves, while Mrs. Stowe's book could not be printed fast enough.

Now that the War Between the States was an actuality, Sarah sought, almost without hope, for some panacea for the country's ills. Her thoughts went back to an earlier dream of hers—the idea of a national Thanksgiving Day, when every family in the country—North and South, East and West—would sit down together, as it were, in grateful acknowledgment of the blessings they all shared.

Sarah could not, of course, remember the first Thanksgiving Day, proclaimed by President George Washington in 1789. She had been only a year old at the time. But she had heard her parents talk of that day and of how all the people of the infant nation had laid aside their work, had prepared feasts and family gatherings, and had knelt in reverent prayers of thanks for their country and its blessings of peace and freedom.

In her childhood home, as in many New England families, her parents had always observed a day of thanksgiving for their harvest. Even as a child Sarah had felt that it would be a wonderful thing if families throughout the country held the same day sacred for that purpose. She had put that feeling into *Northwood* when she said, "We have too few holidays. Thanksgiving, like the Fourth of July, should be considered a national festival and observed by all our people."

Later, as editor of the *Ladies' Magazine*, she had, each November, written about the appropriateness of having family gatherings and feast days during that month. "And what day more appropriate than that chosen by our first President, George Washington, the fourth Thursday of November?" She had printed her favorite mouth-watering recipes, described handsome autumn table decorations, the jolliest games, and suitable songs and recitations to make the day a memorable family affair as well as a national observance.

But with all this gentle persistence, she had not been able to stir the country's consciousness enough to have all the states observe such a day as she proposed.

Soon after becoming editor of the *Lady's Book*, Sarah had taken more active measures. Early each year she began writing letters to the governors of every state and territory, to leading businessmen and industrialists, to Congressmen and editors and the President of the United States, urging them all to promote a national Thanksgiving Day. Some of the states did observe such a day, but it was held on varying dates, with no two states celebrating it on the same day.

Her letters had to be written, addressed and sealed by hand.

At first there were no stamps, and Sarah had to pay varying prices for having those letters delivered. All this meant a great deal of time-consuming work, but Sarah kept at it doggedly throughout the years.

As her influence in the country grew, she became bolder in her advocacy of the holiday. She began to publish the names of the governors who wrote approving of her plan. And she did not hesitate to point out that the absence of a governor's name meant that in that state the day had not been approved. Her editorials started early in the year and appeared each month until November. Year after year Sarah hammered away at the idea. In 1851 all but two states joined in her plan. The following year she wrote:

> Last year twenty-nine states and Territories united in the festival. This year we trust that Virginia and Vermont will come into this arrangement and that the governor of each and all the states will appoint Thursday, the 25th of November, as a Day of Thanksgiving. Twenty-three millions of people sitting down, as it were, to a feast of joy and thankfulness.

She suggested suitable menus for the dinner—roast turkey with savory stuffing, cranberry sauce, and pumpkin pie held the places of honor among the delicious dishes Sarah recommended.

In the Hunters' large dining room, Sarah's whole family assembled each year on the fourth Thursday of November to hold their own private Thanksgiving Day. William, fast becoming noted in the young state of Texas for his handling of land title suits, would come north with his wife and family, to keep the day. Under the affectionate eyes of the parents, the children from Texas would renew acquaintance with their cousins of the East—with Frances' three, Richard, Charles, and little Sarah Hale Hunter, and Horatio's son, another Charles.

Even with a Civil War raging, Sarah kept working for a national Thanksgiving Day through her own example and through her letters. How many hundreds of letters she wrote, how many editorials and poems, Sarah could not have told, for she never kept count.

Then in July of 1863 came the Battle of Gettysburg and the hard-won Union victory that spelled the end of the Confederacy. The hopes of the North soared, and it seemed to observers that there must soon be an end to the fighting in the country. This year, Sarah thought, was the time to ensure peace by uniting both sections of the country in a day of Thanksgiving that the troubles were almost over.

Sarah dipped her pen into the inkpot and began to write. Every summer for the past sixteen years she had written to the Chief Executive, asking him to proclaim a national Thanksgiving Day. President Lincoln must have received at least two such letters; but with the anxiety and the terrible responsibilities of the war upon him, it is no wonder that he had failed to answer. But this time either Sarah's eloquence or his own renewed hope for peace had its effect. On October 1, 1863, Sarah received a letter from William H. Seward, Lincoln's Secretary of State, saying that her letter relative to a national Thanksgiving Day would receive the consideration of the President.

Two days later, on October 3, Lincoln issued the first Thanksgiving Day Proclamation since Washington's, seventy-four years earlier.

When the news came, Sarah was sitting at her desk. Her staff was jubilant, for everyone knew what this meant to her. Led by Godey himself, they came noisily into her office to congratulate her on her triumph.

"At last!" the publisher cried happily, the locks he generally wore brushed over his balding forehead now rumpled and standing erect like feathers. "What perseverance! What a feather in our cap! How! The whole country must acknowledge the *Book's* influence. And it is all due to you, my dear. You never gave up! Sixteen years!"

Sarah had risen when the group entered the room. Now she smiled rather tiredly. "Not sixteen years, sir—thirty-six. I started asking for a national Thanksgiving Day away back in 'twenty-seven."

"Well, you have won the battle——"

Sarah's smile was suddenly bright and warm. "Not yet, sir! One proclamation is not enough. I must now go to work to ensure that there is an annual Presidential Proclamation, which no state will care to ignore. Then, in spite of any troubles that may beset us, the country will be united in love and prayer for at least one day in every year."

17

"I MUST BID FAREWELL"

SARAH WAS TIRED. SHE HAD NOT REALIZED HOW COMPLETELY
worn out she was until, her Thanksgiving Day victory won,
she repeated to herself: "Thirty-six years!" She suddenly
realized that on October 24 she would be seventy-five years
old. She had edited the *Lady's Book* for more than twenty-
six years.

Her many projects, her worry over her beloved, divided
country, her strenuous schedule of writing and editing had
depleted her strength, sapped her reserves of energy. An
especially bitter winter weakened her even more, and for the
first time in her life Sarah found that she was scarcely able to
rise and dress in the morning. Going out into the cold to
reach the office seemed utterly beyond her.

Frances Ann and Josepha, consulting over their mother's
health, reached a decision. Sarah must remain home until
her strength returned. Together they went to the upstairs
room that stretched across the front of Frances' home to deliver their ultimatum.

Sarah, worn and frail, was sitting at her long table-desk. She laid down her pen and regarded her daughters with gentle curiosity.

"You should be lying down, Mother. Better still, you should be in bed," Frances said.

Sarah smiled. "These reviews are the last thing I have to do for this issue of the *Book*. I'll have them finished in an hour."

"But you can't go down to the office!" Josepha exclaimed.

"I didn't plan to go down today. I thought perhaps Richard would deliver the manuscript to Mr. Godey . . ."

"Of course, Mother, Richard will do it gladly. But shouldn't you be resting?" Frances glanced toward the well-upholstered sofa that stood between two windows. From their cages in the sunshine, Sarah's birds chirped merrily.

Sarah shook her head. "I don't feel like lying down, Fanny. But in a little while I'll sit in my rocker and read."

Frances sighed. There was no use arguing. She knew only too well that her mother's gentle courtesy cloaked a very determined will.

That afternoon when Frances' nineteen-year-old son returned from his classes at college, he went up to his grandmother's room to get her copy for the *Book*. He was a tall, handsome young man and Sarah adored him. Richard shook his head reprovingly at the little lady now sitting quietly in her comfortable rocking chair, eating grapes as she read the latest book she had received.

"Mother is worried about you, Mrs. S.J.H.," Richard said affectionately. "Don't you think you ought to let Mr. Godey struggle along without your help for a while?"

Sarah smiled up at her grandson. "As long as I can hold my pen and make it obey my thought, I'll keep on."

Richard bent and lightly kissed the lace cap that covered

Sarah's curls. "Oh, Mrs. S.J.H., you're beyond hope! Where is the stuff for Godey?"

An hour later Sarah heard the rattle of carriage wheels on the cobblestone street beneath her window. Glancing out, she saw her grandson assisting the rotund figure of Louis Godey from the carriage.

How like the dear man to come at once to see her. Her hands flew to her lace cap but it was on straight; the lace at her throat and wrists was fresh and white. Even in her room and not feeling well, Sarah was meticulous about her appearance.

There was a soft tap on the door. At her quiet "Come in, please," it burst open and Godey came puffing in. Sarah laid aside her book and held out her small white hand, only now beginning to show signs of age.

"It's so good of you to come, sir." In all her years of working with the publisher she had maintained an air of friendly formality.

"What do you mean, my dear, by working on the *Book* when you are ill? Can't you rest for a few days at least?"

"A few days, sir? Why, then my copy would be late—and you know how irritated Old Sam gets when he has to set late copy."

"Bother Sam! I can't have you working when you don't feel up to snuff! Goodness knows you've had few enough holidays in the past years. I've been selfish, letting you work yourself to death!" His voice grew husky. "Take a rest, my dear. I'll find stuff to fill the *Book* . . ."

Sarah's eyes were merry. "That's what I fear, sir! That you will fill our *Book* with *stuff!*"

"You're incorrigible! But I mean what I say——"

"Don't say it then," Sarah said firmly. "I'm not helpless yet. And I don't intend to be helpless for many years to come."

Godey paced back and forth across the long room, then he turned to Sarah. "I don't want to see you in the office until Dr. Hunter himself tells you it's all right for you to come. Do you understand, my dear?" He took her hand in his and bent over it gallantly. Sarah saw that his eyes were moist.

"You have been a generous and true friend," she murmured. "I shall not hurry back to the office. But be assured, sir, that, as long as I am able, my manuscripts will be delivered to you in time for each issue."

Sarah did not hurry back to the office. The days stretched into weeks and the weeks into months, the months into years. She found it so much easier to work in that big, sunny room, with her birds and her flowers to keep her company, that she never did go back to the cluttered, noisy office except briefly, now and then, when some crisis called her. Her long desk with its neat piles of papers, the gold pen given to her some years before by an admiring friend, her huge inkpot, the wax and tapers for sealing her letters, the student lamp with its green shade—all were arranged exactly as she liked them. And around her, within call, were her beloved grandchildren. Here she could work in peace, with a quiet happiness she had never known in the busy, crowded office.

It was from this room that Sarah carried on victoriously her campaign against the hated word "female" as used to mean "woman." For a time she tried the humor that she had used against beards, which were now, happily, beginning to go out of fashion again. When she had occasion to use the word "men," she substituted "males." "The lecture was attended by a large number of fashionably dressed males," she wrote. And when some issues of the *Book* were stolen from the post office, she wrote at length about the "males who robbed the mails."

After carrying on the battle in a desultory way for years,

she was gradually seeing the word "woman" or "lady" appear in other journals. But her great triumph came in 1867, when she persuaded Matthew Vassar to eliminate the distasteful word from the name of the new institution he had endowed—the first college for women in America. Over the main door, on the stationery, in the catalogue, the college had been shown as VASSAR FEMALE COLLEGE. Now Mr. Vassar wrote to Sarah that he had had the center stone removed from over the doorway and a plain stone substituted. It was clearly and irrevocably VASSAR   COLLEGE. On stationery and in catalogues the offending word had been inked out.

To the Hunters' home, to see the famous lady editress, "the genius of Philadelphia," came authors, artists, statesmen, inventors—all the notable people who visited Philadelphia. Hannah Murray, for years the Hunter family's maid, grew adept at recognizing famous people and scarcely had to wait for their cards before directing them up the broad stairs to Sarah's room.

And the mail! Letters poured in from every city in the country and from England, France, Germany, Italy, Russia. Sarah's books were read everywhere, her poems recited, her songs sung. She continued to answer all letters herself by hand, and these answers in turn led to further exchanges.

For the next fifteen years Sarah conducted her editorial work, compiled anthologies and annuals, and wrote her books in this bright room. When her health was restored, she went out to see friends, attend lectures, concerts, and church services, and visit the hospitals and schools in which she was still vitally interested.

To accomplish so much, she had to keep regular hours. From nine in the morning till dusk she was at her desk. Her grandchildren would come into the room and settle down quietly to read; they would ask a question and be answered, without disturbing the busy worker. When callers came, she entertained them with no indication that her schedule was being interrupted, for graciousness and tact were, as they had always been, among her chief virtues.

At sundown on Saturday, Sarah's working week was over. For her, Sabbath began at this time, as it had in her childhood home. Sunday was a quiet day, devoted to church, reading, attention to personal correspondence, and the companionship of her family. On Sunday evenings her children and grandchildren gathered in the elegant parlor to talk or sing their favorite songs.

The grandchildren loved these Sunday evenings and often begged Sarah to make them more frequent than just once a week.

"You are always working, Grandmother!" her small namesake, Sarah Hale Hunter, would complain. "When I come upstairs you are always writing or reading. Why do you work so hard all the time?"

Sarah would stroke the child's curls. "There is so much to do, dear, and so short a time to do it in. And then, Grandmother likes to work! Do you think that is odd, darling? Well, I can't imagine what Grandmother would have done without work."

So little time to do the things she wanted to do! Young Sarah and the rest of the family were to remember that phrase some time later.

Louis Godey, sixteen years younger than his editress, had grown more feeble than Sarah. The task of publishing his famous journal had become too great for the ailing man, and in 1877 he sold the *Book* and retired, to live only a few months longer. The new owners took over the magazine in January, 1878, forty years after Sarah had become its editor. She wrote her last editorial for the December, 1877, issue.

She spoke directly to her readers, as she had always done. Frankly, yet modestly, she reviewed her years of work for Godey's, and the reforms for which she had labored, the institutions she had helped to found, the projects she had successfully carried out. Then she went on:

> And now, having reached my ninetieth year, I must bid farewell to my countrywomen, with the hope that this work of half a century may be blessed to the furtherance of their happiness and usefulness in their divinely appointed sphere. New avenues for higher culture and for good works are opening before them, which fifty years ago were unknown. That they may improve these opportunities, and be faithful to their high vocation, is my heartfelt prayer.

Sarah, pale and gentle, attended Godey's funeral. His death was a severe loss to her, for they had worked together happily for forty years. The sale of the *Book*, which they both loved, seemed to write *finis* to their active lives.

Sarah, however, continued to be busy, writing letters, receiving visitors, and attending to her many public duties. Thus sixteen months slipped by, quietly and happily. Then on a bright spring day, April 30, 1879, in the great bed in the alcove of her sunny room, Sarah died.

She had, in her own words, "lived to the last." She had been able to accomplish most of the plans dear to her heart. She had seen the opportunities for women in education and the vocations open wider than they had ever been. On her tombstone might well be carved the words of a character in one of her own stories: *Do not grieve that I am at rest, but rouse up all your energies for the work that is before you.* Or those from her last editorial:

And now I must bid farewell to my countrywomen.

BIBLIOGRAPHY

Allen, Hervey. *Israfel.* Farrar and Rinehart, New York, 1934.

Burt, Struthers. *Philadelphia, Holy Experiment.* Doubleday, Doran, New York, 1945.

Catton, Bruce, Ed. *American Heritage.* American Heritage Publishing Company, New York, October, 1958; December, 1957.

Edes, Sam. "Historical Sketch of Newport, N.H." Speech given at unveiling of Sarah J. Hale Memorial at Newport, August 29, 1929.

Finley, Ruth E. *The Lady of Godey's.* Lippincott, Philadelphia, 1931.

Ford, Henry, Pub. *The Story of Mary and Her Little Lamb.* Henry Ford, Dearborn, Michigan, 1928.

Gilman, Arthur. *The Story of Boston.* G. P. Putnam's Sons, New York, 1894.

Hale, Sarah Josepha Buell. *Flora's Interpreter.* B. B. Musey, Boston, 1852.

————. *Genius of Oblivion and Other Poems.* Jacob B. Moore, Concord, Mass., 1823.

————. *Ladies' Wreath.* Marsh, Capen & Lyon, Boston, 1837.

————. *Liberia.* Harper's, New York, 1853.

————. *Northwood.* Bowles and Dearborn, Boston, 1827.

————. *Poems for Our Children.* Marsh, Capen & Lyon, Boston, 1850.

————. *Woman's Record.* Harper & Brothers, New York, 1874.

Hale, Sarah Josepha Buell, Ed. *The Lady's Book.* Louis A. Godey, Philadelphia. Various issues from January, 1938, to December, 1877.

————. *Ladies' Magazine.* Putnam & Hunt, Boston, 1828-37.

Hanaford, Phebe A. *Daughters of America.* True & Company, Augusta, Maine, 1882.

185

Hudson, Frederic. *History of Journalism.* New York, 1873.

Mott, Frank Luther. *History of American Magazines.* D. Appleton, New York, 1930.

Packard, Professor. *History of Bunker Hill Monument.* Privately printed, 1853.

Parrington, Vernon Luther. *Main Currents of American Thought.* Harcourt, Brace & Co., New York, 1927.

Strong, Joanna, and Leonard, Tom B. *The World's Great Heroines.* Hart, New York, 1951.

Tassin, Algernon. *The Magazine in America.* Dodd, Mead, 1916.

Wheeler (no initial). *A History of Newport, New Hampshire.* 1868.

Wood, James Playsted. *Magazines in the United States.* Ronald Press, New York, 1956.